MW00654599

Coming Together

Embracing your Core Desires for Sexual
Fulfillment and Long-Term Compatibility

Danielle Harel, PhD & Celeste Hirschman, MA

Coming Together

Embracing your Core Desires for Sexual
Fulfillment and Long-Term Compatibility

Danielle Harel, PhD & Celeste Hirschman, MA

www.CelesteAndDanielle.com
www.SomaticaInstitute.com

Published by Somatica Press, all rights reserved
Copyright © 2020 Danielle Harel and Celeste Hirschman
ISBN 978-0-578-59265-7
First Edition

Cover Design: Yair 'Jay' Harel

This book is not intended as a substitute for the medical
advice of physicians. The reader should regularly consult a
physician in matters relating to his/her health and
particularly with respect to any symptoms that may require
diagnosis or medical attention.

Somatica Press

Acknowledgments

We knew we had a lot to say, but it's hard to believe that we have actually completed a third book. Writing a book is a huge undertaking and we are so grateful to those who have helped and supported us in the process. First we want to thank our families for their constant encouragement of our quest to make the world a sexier and more connected place.

Thank you Yair 'Jay' Harel for your unwavering commitment to Somatica and your amazing talent in creating the cover design and the layout of the book. Dimitry Yakoushkin for your invaluable feedback on the content of the book. Danika Renee for your keen editing eye - your brilliant suggestions on content and structure helped to make the book what it is and you weeded out more typos than we'd like to admit.

Jon Hull - thank you for generously giving us feedback on all three of our books and for making sure that the book was clear and cogent. Christopher Simmons for your birds eye view which helped you see some issues that those too close to the project inevitably missed. Finally, to Magick Altman for being a fabulous all-around editor and fantastic mom.

While most books are a labor of love, this one is a labor of sex. Thank you all for your help in birthing more pleasure into the world.

Table of Contents

Part III

Welcome to Your Desires

A healthy sex life is one of the most important keys to long-term relationship success. Great sex deepens the emotional bond between two people, increases happiness, and helps you make it through the day-to-day challenges of life. When sex isn't happening, it often becomes the focus of fights, disconnection, and dissatisfaction. As one of our clients put it - when sex is good, it becomes 10% of the relationship and when it isn't, it becomes 90% of the relationship.

Women come into our office complaining of low desire. Men begin to lose their erections or express that they prefer to stay home and masturbate to their favorite porn instead of going out and looking for a partner. Couples come in who have suffered in sexless relationships for many years and tell us in hushed voices about their boring sexual routines. Couples who love and are attracted to each other share their bafflement as to why their sex lives aren't thriving.

Erectile dysfunction (ED), low desire, and porn dependence may seem like functional barriers, but, more often, they are the result of people not being in touch with what they really want sexually. It's like their bodies or their psyches are saying: "I'm not getting the sex that I really want, so I don't really want to have sex." It's no wonder so many couples end up in sexless relationships.

Sex therapists, coaches, doctors, and sex experts each present their own separate solutions to sexual problems focusing largely on technique and one-size-fits-all approaches. Unfortunately, techniques don't get to the heart of what people are really looking for from their sexual connections. One size does not fit all since people's desires are very unique.

As sex and relationship coaches with 30 years of combined experience, we have seen every sexual issue. What may be surprising is that almost all of the problems that have to do with sex can be addressed by a single solution: understanding your Core Desires. Understanding your Core Desires is the opposite of a one-size-fits-all approach. It is discovering the unique set of feelings and experiences you want to have. We go to sex to feel something - whether it is powerful, adored, competent, etc. In order for your sex life to thrive, your Core Desires must be discovered and fulfilled.

Considering our society's lack of a nuanced understanding of desire, it is no mystery that people are struggling. Let's take a lack of sexual compatibility as an example. Often people have searched for answers in couple's therapy, tried deepening their communication (many times with great success on the relationship front), tried all the latest sexy toys, retreats and couple's vacations, and even tried experiential workshops - from tantra to kink and everything in between - without any long-term change in their sexual connection. This is because, unless the approach uncovers your Core Desires, it is not going to solve the problem.

It could be the case that tantra, a new sex toy, kink, or even just the fact that their partner was willing to try something new might work for some people. If your Core Desire is around novelty, just trying something new might spark up some excitement. Or, if one of your Core Desires is teamwork, going to a workshop together might meet that need. Likewise, some people have Core Desires around power, so a kink workshop would be great, while others like to feel their sex is spiritual, so tantra might get them aroused.

The problem with most approaches is that they offer surface solutions. This means each person's foundational Core Desires are never fully accessed or properly shared. Imagine if this couple kept having tantric or kinky sex, but the novelty wore off for one, and the other didn't feel that team feeling anymore once the workshop adventure was over. In a matter of months or even weeks, they would be back to square one, even more at a loss as to why their sex lives are not thriving.

Or, imagine that they went to a kink workshop, but only one of them was turned on by the content of the workshop. They might start shaming each other, or feeling like it is unfair that only one person is getting their needs met. With the help of Coming Together, you can share and teach each other your actual turn-ons while discovering and honoring differences. This is the pathway to an exciting, sustainable sex life. It is also the pathway to much more openness and intimacy in your relationship.

Don't get confused. While it is sometimes possible to get turned on at the beginning of a new sexual connection by experiences that do not touch on your Core Desires, getting your Core Desires met is essential to your long-term sexual satisfaction.

In this book, we will illustrate the steps of how to reach sexual compatibility as a couple:

1.   Learn what turns each of you on - your Core Desires

2. Communicate these Core Desires in a way each of you can understand and relate to

3. Fully accept each other's Core Desires while knowing that you can also have your boundaries

4. Go through the process of learning your partner's Core Desires and how to play them out in an experiential way (your Hottest Sexual Movies)

5. Bridge differences in how you want to have sex and learn to take turns if your sexual desires are vastly different from one another's

Discovering your Core Desires might seem simple and straightforward, yet people are continually struggling with sexual issues because they don't really know how to do it. If this is your experience, go easy on yourself - the information available out there about sexual arousal is pretty terrible, and most professionals don't know how to help. Additionally, even if you know what you want, the next steps can be daunting.

Finding a way to talk about it, feeling safe articulating it, and then knowing how to teach your partner about it, can all be challenging because of the shame and sex-negativity in our society. Creating a safe space for you and your partner to share who you really are as sexual beings is one of the most valuable gifts you can give each other. The vulnerability of sharing these desires deepens trust, intimacy, and emotional connection.

While most advice suggests communication as the end-all-be-all of transformation in your sex life, just talking about it isn't enough. Whether you are in a long-term relationship or out there in the dating world, if you really want to have the most mind-blowing and deeply fulfilling sex possible, you have to know what feelings you want to have during sex and be able to teach others how to take you there. The process of teaching a partner can be challenging and it is essential to be gentle and teach experientially.

Additionally, you both must have the patience to go through this learning curve together. Sound difficult or scary? Once you engage it can be fun and exciting, particularly if you can leave judgment at the door and go into it with curiosity and compassion. Remember, you don't have to do anything you don't want to do, and the fact that your partner may have different desires than you doesn't mean you have to change who you are.

Before we dive more deeply into how to discover both your own and your partner's Core Desires, we think it is important to talk about the three reasons why this process is not common knowledge - why we don't have a good collective understanding or conversation around our Core Desires.

Reason 1: The Myth that Sex is "Just Supposed to Happen"

As a society, we have the extremely damaging belief that sex is just supposed to happen (and, moreover, be immediately great). In movies, television, and romance novels, we see two people falling into each other's arms and, without a word, having mind-blowing sex that completely fulfills each of them. Whether they end in a fade-out, or satisfied side-by-side panting, there is never a moment before, during, or after where they say, "Hey, I'd really like you to..." or, "Wow, that was great, and you know what would make it even better next time..." or, even, "You know, I'm really attracted to you, but for sex to be satisfying for me, I'm gonna need a little bit of..."

This idea that sex is just supposed to happen - and be great when it does - means that we are not supposed to have a conversation, we are supposed to just find "the one" that will be a perfect match and will be able to know what we need without having to ask. This damaging myth has gotten in the way of so many potentially compatible couples, leaving them endlessly disappointed, living in a sexless relationship or moving on to someone else.

Reason 2: There are Socially Acceptable Sexual Desires and Other Desires that are Judged and Shamed

The second, more painful and insidious reason is that our culture has a set of specific sexual desires that are seen as acceptable and others that are not. As a society, we exalt monogamous couples made up a stereotypical man and woman participating in romantic or passionate sex with some occasional male dominance sprinkled in to add some edginess or taboo. The people in these stories are generally thin, able-bodied, and heterosexual with normal lives, jobs, etc. Any erotic desire or experience that falls outside of these parameters is rarely depicted in media. When they are depicted, they are often shown as aberrations. People who have shamed and unacceptable desires are often shown as criminals or social outcasts who are ultimately punished for their digressive behaviors.

Desires between same-sex couples or transgender folks, non-monogamy, multiple-partner sex, female dominance, fetishes, or anything else outside of societal norms is generally ridiculed or made to look comical, leading to hiding or potential social ostracization. The requirement that people have socially acceptable sex prevents a more open and comprehensive conversation and leaves many people's desires out of the picture. This makes it very difficult for people to explore, accept, or come out about what they really desire sexually.

Reason 3: Sex is Trivialized or Pathologized

Another reason that we are not having an in-depth and nuanced conversation around sexual desires is that our culture thinks of sex as trivial and inessential to our happiness or to a well-rounded life. While your sexual self-acceptance and self-expression is an important key to your confidence, aliveness, and overall joy in life, many of our cultural beliefs will end up making you feel like thinking about sex and talking about sex is an indication that you lack more meaningful pursuits.

You can see these beliefs in the ways society pathologizes people who are deeply interested in sex. They are called nymphomaniacs or perverts. Our society pathologized desires as "weird" or "fetishes" and shames folks that have desires different from what is most socially acceptable. People who masturbate frequently or have multiple partners are labeled sex addicts. The level to which we are willing to label a deep interest in sex as an addiction is an indication of how uncomfortable our society is with sex.

In the face of these three reasons, it is no wonder we don't have a very nuanced, broad, or helpful erotic lexicon.

How Coming Together is Different

In Coming Together, we will help you understand what's at the core of many sexual challenges, including sexless marriages, low desire, erectile dysfunction, and porn dependency. We will offer you a deeper understanding of what helps you maintain attraction and sexual compatibility beyond the honeymoon period. We will give practical tools to discover the feelings you want to have and teach you how to write, direct, and star in your own Hottest Sexual Movies.

While some books have offered basic tools of self-discovery in this area, we are going to walk you through the step-by-step process to break down all the necessary aspects of learning about your Core Desires and Hottest Sexual Movies so that you can accept your desires, teach your partner what you want, and fully realize your erotic potential. This will inevitably lead to you having a more exciting and fulfilling sexual and emotional life.

Part I

Discover your Core Desires

The Shaping of Your Core Desires

You have particular feelings that you want to have during sex. Everyone has them. Most people think that an orgasm during sex means that the sex was good. However, if you look at your sexual experiences deeply, you will notice that orgasms can often be the effect of great sex, (or simply hard work), but they are generally not the cause.

The intense desire and arousal that sometimes brings you to orgasm are caused by a sexual experience that makes you feel something that you really want to feel. Feeling what you really want to feel is what makes some of your sexual experiences far more fulfilling than others. When people talk about their most exciting, intense, and outstanding sexual experiences, they usually won't mention whether they had an orgasm or not. Instead, their eyes glow as they describe the feeling they had when their partner met them in a very specific way that touched their most vulnerable longings.

The set of feelings you want to have, which we call your Core Desires, is the key that unlocks your arousal and your orgasm, yet it's unlikely that you've ever deeply explored its essence or its importance to your pleasure. Just imagine how amazingly hot your sex life could be if you had the awareness and a language to let your partner know exactly how to bring you to your highest erotic heights and how to bring them to theirs.

Before you go on the journey of discovering your Core Desires, let's take a look at where your Core Desires come from. Their development started long before you ever had or even considered having a partner. The deepest needs in your erotic life were shaped by your experiences with the people around you when you were a child. Sometimes they are complex.

One inspiration for our understanding of what makes sex exciting comes from a brilliant San Francisco psychotherapist by the name of Jack Morin. He presented his theory and findings in his book "The Erotic Mind." Dr. Morin studied the fantasies and peak erotic experiences of numerous participants and found that their desires were shaped by childhood experiences that had a combination of arousal and an obstacle. He asserted that it was the frustration of certain desires that shaped our deepest turn-ons, and called these turn-ons *Core Erotic Theme*. He also found that these desires remained a person's central sexual desires for the rest of their lives.

In working with hundreds of clients over decades, we have also seen that people's sexual desires are shaped in childhood. While Morin focused on obstacles, what we have seen more commonly is that erotic desires are a direct attempt to soothe early childhood wounds including everything from our lack of getting a certain set of core needs met to experiences of trauma. For this reason, we call people's deepest sexual needs their "Core Desires."

Client after client has shared challenging childhood experiences that relate directly to their Core Desires. A good example was our client, Bill. When Bill was a child, he had an unusual skin disease: his skin would crack and blister, and would often get infected. His well-meaning parents were worried about exacerbating the problem and, as a result, almost never touched him except to put ointment on his body. When we met Bill, his adult fantasies were all about being licked and bitten and caressed all over. He said he wanted every inch of him to be embraced and adored. For someone who was barely touched as a child, it makes sense that his erotic fantasies would revolve around being wanted, desired, and engaged in a very visceral way.

While Bill's history was a more rare experience, another client of ours, Mary, shared a much more common imprinting experience - a lack of parental attention. Mary was the child of a workaholic father and a codependent mother, who constantly focused on taking care of her husband. Neither parent focused on Mary's needs or feelings, and she described her childhood experience as "feeling completely invisible." Later, as an adult, her most common fantasy was dressing up in a gorgeous negligee and doing an exotic dance for a huge audience of adoring and aroused fans. They would stand with their erections at attention, looking her up and down, never tiring of her or her beauty.

It might seem surprising that your sexual desires were shaped so early on in your life before many people have had any direct erotic experiences. However, the research by Dr. Morin, the clinical experience we have with our clients, and the stories our clients have shared, clearly indicate this link. In some ways, this can be very relieving. If you have no choice about what turns you on, the best approach to your turn-ons is to fully accept and celebrate them and then to try to get them met in safe, consensual ways. This can be challenging for some turn-ons more than others.

If your Core Desires were shaped by particularly painful or traumatic experiences, you may also feel understandable sadness and anger about not having control of how your desires were shaped. While we truly understand how painful this can be, we want to offer you hope that differentiating your current adult desires from the shaping of those desires, and fully embracing and learning how to have them met in a celebratory way, can add a tremendous amount of healing and joy to your life.

In addition to the ways that our Core Desires were shaped in our childhood, research has also shown that the way we want to enact them, can be shaped by our culture - everything from gender expectations to our political belief systems. In his book Tell Me What You Want, Justin Lehmiller shares findings from the largest study done to date on the sexual fantasies of adults in the United States. The study showed, for example, that conservatives were much more likely to fantasize about breaking taboos while liberal fantasies incorporated more power play. It also showed that women had more emotion-based fantasies than men, and men had more taboo-breaking fantasies than women.

The bottom line is that your Core Desires are not changeable, the things that turn you on the most will always turn you on the most. Some people feel like their Core Desires have changed over their lifetime. This may be because there are two pathways to get to the same feeling - resolution, or repetition with agency. We will go deeper into these two pathways later. Regardless, all paths lead to the same root desires, but the kinds of sex you need to have in order to get these desires met may look completely different.

Coming Together is full of practical tools to help you have a better sex life. After working with thousands of clients, we are ready to help you discover and get your Core Desires met. As a final note, your freedom of choice is very important. Once you find out what you really, really want, the choice of what you want to do with this information is yours. For example, there may be ways to have your Core Desires met that feel better or more comfortable for you, and there may be some turn-ons you never want to explore any further than acknowledging that they are there.

Just knowing and accepting yourself can be deeply satisfying whether you decide to pursue your Core Desires or not. It is also possible to have arousal and excitement even if your Core Desires are not being touched. You are the expert on how to live your life; we are just here to support you in finding the right path for you with as much love, gentleness, and self-acceptance as possible.

Get Your Head in the Game

Before you start exploring your Core Desires and how to share them with your partner(s), it is important to embrace the right attitude and approach. You can begin by developing self-awareness so that you can study your own desires and motivations. Get curious and open-minded about your desires. Before involving your partner, take some time to look at your internal sexual self on your own. It will be important to understand and accept yourself before trying to share with a partner.

Become a Self-Detective

We can spend endless hours of our lives studying, guessing, and gossiping about everyone else's motives and desires, but we rarely take time to explore our own, especially when it comes to our sex lives. You can start this process by gathering some data from your own life. What turns you on might be sparked by romantic encounters, experiences full of passion and intrigue, spiritual connections, or playing with dominance and submission or kink. As you explore, we recommend doing some journaling to really pinpoint your Core Desires.

Take a Curious and Non-Judgmental Attitude

Before you start to explore all of this, the most important part of self-detecting is taking a curious and non-judgmental attitude. You may find that some of what turns you on is more accepted by society and other parts of what turns you on are less accepted. If any of your thoughts make you feel ashamed or guilty, remember, they are just part of your erotic imagination and you may or may not ever decide to act on them.

What if your Core Desires aren't socially acceptable? For example, as a woman, if you want to feel desired, loved, taken, connected, adored, feminine, or cherished, those are highly socially acceptable feelings to want to have. As a man, if you want to feel desired, powerful, masculine, or competent, no one will bat an eyelash.

However, if you are either gender and you want to feel degraded, punished, scared, cruel, shaming, like the opposite gender - or any other feelings that you might think of as negative - you might fear that others will not accept your fantasies. And, sadly, you might be right. Historically, some sexual desires have been thought of as so deviant that they were considered to be diagnosable psychological illnesses, while others have simply received the moniker "perverted."

In our work with clients, in our training classes, and in the world in general, we hold a non-judgemental space where any feelings that you want to have are celebrated. Once we help people figure out what they want to feel sexually, we help them find ways to enact those feelings that are safe and consensual. This could mean anything from simply fantasizing about them during sex to sharing those fantasies with partners, or enacting them sexually in a way that doesn't harm themselves or others. We also help people decide if and when they want to share these fantasies with partners, depending on whether they feel safe enough to do so.

Since we can't have every single one of you in our office, we want you to create this non-judgmental space for yourself. Learning how to get to your highest states of arousal is a wonderful thing, as is accepting yourself as you are. The best way to cultivate self-acceptance and to begin the process of self-discovery is to embrace the idea that thoughts and fantasies are different than actions.

If Your Fantasies Clash with Your Personal Belief System

Some people have Core Desires that are antithetical to their politics or beliefs about how people should behave in the world. This can make it difficult to fully embrace your desires. Perhaps what turns you on is something you'd never actually want to happen to anyone out in the world, and the guilt prevents you from experiencing your arousal. This is actually quite common. Many people are aroused by things that are taboo or that involve power differences.

Let's take the example of being a feminist. If you are a feminist, that's wonderful. Who wouldn't want men and women to be treated equally and women to be given the full amount of dignity and respect afforded to men? Our Core Desires, however, do not necessarily conform to our politics. You might be a feminist and be turned on by feeling submissive or coerced; you may even have rape fantasies, which are quite common among women.

As a teenager, one of our clients had seen a film with a very explicit rape scene in it. While watching the scene, she felt extremely aroused and went up to her room to masturbate. After she orgasmed, she felt a huge rush of shame. She didn't understand how she could be turned on by a woman being harmed, she felt ashamed for having these fantasies, and she started to shut down around her sexuality. Ultimately, with our help, she discovered that her upbringing shamed her so strongly around her desire for sex, that the idea of rape (not actually being raped) allowed her to imagine a sexual experience in which she had no choice. This allowed her to feel sexual without feeling responsible for wanting sex so she could surrender to her arousal.

As we talked with her, we explained why it is ok that her politics and her turn-ons clashed and how she could reconcile this discrepancy in her life. The bottom line is that you do not have any control over what turns you on. You may imagine these fantasies while masturbating or role-play rape as a way to bring you to orgasm; after all, it is completely harmless to run a fantasy in your head or play it out consensually with a partner in bed. This does not mean that you want women to actually be raped, and you can continue to fight for women's equality.

We also had a male client who was a feminist. He felt ashamed that his fantasy was about dominating powerful women. At the same time, he found a woman to marry who was his intellectual, social, and professional equal. He supported her in her career and took an equal part in child-rearing. They learned to enjoy this fantasy together once they realized that what they did in the bedroom did not have any bearing on how they treated each other in day-to-day life.

If the Feelings You Want to Have are Rooted in Trauma

One of the most challenging situations we face in working with clients is when their Core Desires developed from some kind of trauma - especially childhood sexual trauma. While it is not always the case that sexual abuse will shape your Core Desires, we have seen it enough times in our office to conclude that it is probably quite common.

If you experienced childhood sexual abuse, incest, or some other sexual, emotional, or physical trauma as a child, your Core Desires may be related to those experiences. Sometimes, your Core Desires are to have the opposite experience of your trauma - taking power or feeling cared-for, and other times, they develop as a desire for something that feels more like a repetition of the traumatic experiences.

This can be particularly painful because it may feel like your abuser has left some indelible mark on you and that they somehow still have control over you. We have helped clients look at it in a different way. As an adult, you can reclaim your turn-ons from these early traumas. Through this reclamation, you can become an empowered adult with the agency to choose how you want to play these Core Desires out and with whom. This is the opposite of being controlled by your abuser. You can find partners who respect your body and your boundaries and who will stop and check-in if you use your safeword.

We will talk more about negotiating around boundaries and safewords later in our discussion of your Hottest Sexual Movie. Suffice it to say, many of the ways people play in different BDSM communities rest on the idea that you can turn old pain into present-day pleasure. You can embrace your deepest longings and have the most fulfilling, healing, and hottest sex you've ever had. Embracing it and removing shame and stigma around your Core Desires, and particularly those that are associated with early trauma, also helps you feel like a whole human being.

Our client Cathy's story is one of abuse and reclamation. When Cathy was six years old, she was caught masturbating by using her hand over her clothes while in her bedroom. Her mother slapped her face, took her to the bathroom, placed her in the shower fully clothed, and ran cold water over her while aggressively washing her hands with soap. While she was washing her, her mother yelled at her, "You are dirty and disgusting, I don't want to ever see you do that again. Where did you learn to touch yourself there?" and many other things that Cathy could not remember.

As Cathy grew up, her sex life evolved to incorporate elements from this childhood event. Cathy's most arousing sex involves feeling both guided, dirty, and caught. She liked to role-play with partners that she was a little girl, and they were teaching her how to masturbate. Sometimes she wanted her partner to "catch" her touching herself and tell her how dirty and naughty she was and that she was only allowed to do it in front of them, but never by herself. When they "caught" her, she also wanted them to slap her face and spank her.

When she first came to us, she felt a lot of shame, anger, and frustration for having these desires. She felt like her mother was still controlling her life in some way. We helped her see that she had taken a traumatic event and was now playing it out on her own terms consensually with partners who excited her and were excited by her fantasies.

You may have disturbing thoughts that arouse you, but you can still always choose to have sex that is safe and consensual. We want you to explore and embrace your erotic imagination separate from any actions you might take. Later in the book, we will talk about how to get the feelings you want to have, whatever they are, in ways that are safe and consensual. We will also teach you how to share your Core Desires with partners in a way that they will most likely be able to hear them.

Take Your Personal Journey First

While increasing arousal and compatibility with your partner may be a motivator in all of this, we strongly recommend you begin this journey privately. By creating a safe space of privacy to discover what turns you on, you can let go of the pressure to conform to what you imagine your partner wants you to be.

Sometimes, we want to be compatible or to have the acceptance of our partner so badly that we don't dare to really discover what we want. You can look at it this way: no matter what you discover about your turn-ons, you still have the choice about what kinds of sex you want to have and with whom. Even if you never act on anything that you learn about yourself from this exploration, just the experience of knowing yourself and accepting yourself will increase your confidence and enhance your self-love.

Connect to Your Body

The first step in finding your Core Desires is to become present in your body. The reason you need to connect to your body is that your mind will have all sorts of ideas and explanations, but you will need to listen to your body - particularly feelings of arousal or shut down - to understand what turns you on and what does not. In this discovery, you may find that you have been having sex that is just right for you or that you have been putting up with sex that does not actually meet any of your needs; that is in fact, negative or harmful to you in some way.

One of the best ways to become present in your body is through breathwork and connecting to your sensations. Since our society rewards us for our thoughts more than our sensations and feelings, so much of our lives are lived in our heads. While you can get a lot of information about your fantasies through thinking about what turns you on, if you cannot feel your body at all, you may be missing a very important source of information.

Later, as we ask you to think about and visualize your turn-ons, being able to feel changes in your bodily arousal, energy, and excitement will be very important. The more you are engaged with your whole body, and the more in touch you are with your bodily arousal, the more easily you will be able to distinguish your turn-ons because you will feel tingling in your genitals (or other body parts) when something delicious is happening!

The following breathwork session will help you get in touch with your erotic body. While practices such as yoga or meditation use breathwork to help deepen mindfulness and embodiment, this breathwork session will take you directly to erotic embodiment. The more embodied you are, the more your body will tell you when you have touched on your Core Desires.

 Exercise:
Erotic Breath

Find a place where you feel comfortable and have some privacy. It is best to be sitting or lying down.

You do not need to be in any kind of meditation pose for this practice and it might actually be more helpful for you to have back support. If you are lying down, you can lie flat or lie with your knees bent - find a position that helps you feel the most relaxed and connected to your pelvic floor.

Follow this 5-step process to deepen your erotic embodiment and presence:

1. Close your eyes and take some nice, slow, deep breaths through your mouth. We encourage mouth breathing because it can sometimes help you bring the breath more deeply into your body. However, there is no right way to breathe - if you find yourself much more connected and comfortable when you breathe through your nose, feel free to do that.

2. Send the breath toward your chest, allowing the muscles in your chest to relax, release, and flow with the breath. If it helps you aim your breath, feel free to put your hand on your chest and breathe toward your hand. Do not force relaxation here; this is more about allowing the breath and experiencing your body than trying to make any particular type of change.

3. Next, send the breath down to your belly and allow the belly to rise and fall with the breath. Again, you may want to place your hand on your belly and feel your hand rising and falling. Tune into your body and allow

any thoughts to float by while continuing to focus on your breath and your self-touch.

4. Finally, send the breath all the way down to your pelvic floor - your penis or vulva (or whatever you call your genitals) and your perineum. Feel the breath go all the way down to your anal muscles allowing all of the muscles in your pelvic floor to open and relax. You may want to place your hand on your pelvis for a deeper connection.

5. Once you are breathing all the way down, it is time to enhance your connection to sensations in your pelvic floor. You will do this by squeezing your pelvic floor muscles (or PC muscles - also sometimes referred to as doing Kegels). Instead of thinking of this as a strengthening exercise, we want you to focus on its erotic potential. As you breathe in, take a nice deep squeeze of your vaginal or penile muscles like you are stopping yourself from peeing and then, on the out-breath, release these muscles. Do this breathing and releasing at least 20 times to get the full effect.

Bonus step: Take some time while you are breathing and squeezing the muscles in your pelvic floor to caress different parts of your body - your arms, your face, your chest, your belly, your genitals, and enjoy the sensuality of touching and connecting with yourself physically while breathing. Invite any arousal that may come, but don't feel like you have to feel aroused. This breathwork will help you be more present and connected even if you are not feeling any arousal.

Once you have taken your final deep breath with squeezes, keep your eyes closed and notice how your body feels. See if you feel more deeply connected to yourself and your erotic body. Now, open your eyes and begin to look around the room while keeping this connection with yourself on the inside. Notice if the room around you seems a bit more vivid or if you feel more aliveness in your body as you keep this self-connection flowing.

All Roads Lead to Moan

Now that you are more connected to your body, you can use it as a gauge to see what turns you on and what doesn't. As you engage your erotic imagination, your body will help you start to get a better idea of your Core Desires. There are so many ways to explore your erotic imagination. In the next several sections, we will take you on a journey to help you pinpoint your turn-ons.

If one road doesn't get you there, don't despair. You might need a different pathway to self-understanding. The most important thing to remember is that the focus here is not to identify the particular sexual experiences you want to have (we will get to that later). Instead, seek to understand what kinds of feelings you want to have. You may need to think of your most common fantasies or best experiences to help you unearth those feelings.

Find Out What You Want to Feel

The journey of discovering what you want to feel from sex can take some time. When we first discovered the concept of Core Desires, we began to explore what it was that really got each of us going. Throughout our time working with clients, theorizing, and teaching about them, our understanding of our own Core Desires became more specific, clear, and nuanced.

Celeste started out thinking her Core Desire was coercion but later realized that the feelings she wanted to have were a combination of feeling special and powerful. The early confusion came because Celeste was not actually in any of her fantasies and her fantasies all contained non-consensual acts that involved coercion. The interesting part was that, when she fantasized, she imagined the thoughts of the person in the power position (as opposed to the powerless position). Thus, her fantasies were about feeling ultimately powerful over someone who is ultimately powerless. In her sexual experiences, she wanted her partners to see her as the most special, which is also a form of feeling powerful. She realized she likes to feel approved of, complimented, and to know she is the most amazing lover a person has ever had.

Danielle started out thinking her Core Desire was to feel desired, as many of the fantasies and hottest sexual experiences she had contained an element of being desired in them. However, as she continued to explore and consider what really made sex hot for her, she realized that what she wanted was acceptance. She wanted every inch of her body to be accepted and all of her ideas and fantasies to be fully celebrated and embraced. She wanted her pace to be enjoyed and encouraged and her lovers to take all the time in the world to please and arouse her and to get their pleasure from doing so.

You may have never deeply considered what turns you on, which is very understandable. Again, our society does not encourage this type of self-exploration, especially for women. You have been taught to expect that falling into bed with that special someone will offer all of the arousal and satisfaction you need. With that said, don't be hard on yourself if you really have no idea about what turns you on.

Also, if you don't have any overtly sexual fantasies, that doesn't mean that you don't have fantasies. Common beliefs about what constitutes a fantasy may make you discount experiences that are actually very arousing for you. Anything that causes arousal or deepens your desire for or interest in sex is a fantasy. When we ask a client what turns them on, they usually tell us something about what positions they like or where they want to have sex. However, the sexual position or location a person chooses is rarely the key to their arousal (unless of course their whole fantasy life is organized around a single position or location). To understand what really turns you on, you will need to know what you want to feel.

If you look at it this way, a sexual fantasy may be that your partner texts you during the day while you are at work and asks you how you are doing. Because you feel cared for by them, you start to get turned on and begin to get excited about connecting intimately with them when you get home. This counts as a sexual fantasy and is something you could tell your partner you need when they ask what you want sexually.

Even if you do have some idea of what you desire, exploring it step-by-step can really help you discover the intricacies and have empathy for your partner's desires, which will inevitably be different from your own in some ways. Try to be gentle with yourself and your partner throughout this process. Once you have a better idea, you will be able to craft the sex life that suits you the best.

In the same way that our understanding of our Core Desires has shifted over time, as you begin to consider, play with, and explore your own Core Desires, your understanding will likely shift and deepen over time as well. For this reason, we invite you to keep an open attitude and consider each of your discoveries as hypotheses. You can continue to test them out and your understanding of them will likely evolve.

So what does it mean to focus on identifying your Core Desires? It means, when you go to sex, you might want to feel some of the following feelings: *powerful, taken, degraded, surprised, in danger, cared for, precious, teased, indulgent, loved, denied, adored, abused, seen, desirable, powerless, known, punished, or accepted.* Throughout the book, we have italicized the many different feelings you might want to get from sex so you will be able to share your Core Desires by telling your partner(s) what you want to feel.

We have included a more exhaustive list in the visualization below. To get a better idea of what we mean by your Core Desires, here are some examples:

❖ If you fantasize about sex in public places, this might be a fantasy of being

- so *desirable* your partner would have sex with you anywhere
- *seen* or *watched* (exhibitionism)
- *in danger* (of being caught)
- *naughty* (getting away with something)
- *free*

❖ If your fantasy is of your partner surprising you by taking you to a five-course dinner at your favorite, fancy restaurant, it might be a fantasy of being

- *cared for* (they planned it and/or are paying for it)
- *known* (they knew it was your favorite restaurant)
- *indulgent* (five-course and fancy)
- *excited* (from being surprised)

❖ If your fantasy is coming on someone's face, it might be a fantasy of

- feeling *fully accepted*
- *degrading the other person*
- being *dirty, messy,* or *naughty*
- feeling *proud* or *lucky* (because you have an enthusiastic partner)
- *possessiveness* (the person is yours and you can do anything to them)

As you are thinking and writing about the topic of what turns you on, always try to get to the bottom of what you want to feel!

Reach Beneath the Surface

If you already have some idea of what acts you like to engage in, things you like your partner to do or say during sex or things you like to do to your partner, you may get even deeper insights by taking a visualization journey into your arousal.

 Exercise:
Visualization to Find Your Core Desires

Start with the breathwork session above. As you move into the part with the pelvic squeezes, begin noticing your body and how it feels. Imagine a hot sexual experience that you've had or that you want to have or some fantasy that really turns you on. Let your mind land on an experience or a fantasy that would most likely make you come.

As you breathe and squeeze your pelvic muscles, embody this scene as much as possible and paint all of the details you can. What has built you up to it? Where are you? Who is there with you - one other person, a whole stadium full of people? What does the place look like? What scents do you smell? Are you inside or outside? Is it daytime or at night? Is it lit? With what - candles, a chandelier, a spotlight?

What are you wearing? What are other people wearing? What are the actions? Are they happening to you or are you doing things to someone else? Are you watching as others engage with each other? Let yourself fully paint the entire scene, and focus on the parts that turn you on the most.

As you are seeing and experiencing the scene with as many details as possible, start to notice the feelings that you are having. What feelings matter the most to you? Take a moment to notice which of the following feelings seem to create a response in your body. Notice whether the response is arousal or something else. You may feel:

Loved, Calm, Degraded, Powerful, Free, Precious, Beautiful, Connected, Considered, Playful, Fun, Vulnerable, Cared for, Alive, Creative, Taken care of, Reassured, Pushed, Received, Played With, Dominant, Collaborative, Exploitative, Manipulative, Taken Advantage Of, Enjoyed, Naughty, Afraid/Scared, Penetrated, Approved of, Forced, Encouraged, Desired, Adventuresome, Ravished, Seen, Dissolved, Shamed, Impressive, Authentic, Consumed, United, Generous, Spiritual, Trusted, Punished, Out of Control, Accepted, Wanted, Not Responsible, Transcendent, Appreciated, In Control, Celebrated, Capable, Sexy, Taken, Probed, Submissive, Understood, Safe, Taboo, Valued, Adored, Secretive, Exposed, Controlled, Feminine, Masculine Cruel, Teased, Violated, Used, Irresistible, Merged, Unattainable, Worshipped, Contained, Pleasing, Mysterious, Supported, Open.

Or, it may be a feeling or feelings that we haven't mentioned here. If so, please add your own feelings to the list.

You might notice that some of the feelings on the list are feelings you might think of as "negative" such as degraded, forced, shamed, or cruel. We will talk more about this later in the book. For now, and just for yourself, see if you can be honest about what you want to feel and try not to judge or shame yourself for it.

You may have several feelings that seem to be at odds with one another or they may all be in alignment. Either way, let all the feelings be there. Let yourself feel these feelings. Let them spread through your body. Now go back to that fantasy and see what in particular makes you feel the feelings.

Is it specific actions or acts, the environment, the relationship between you and others or between those you are watching or who are watching you? Is it a particular type of person or some inanimate object? Is it certain words or phrases? Once you have a good idea of what you want to feel, take one last deep breath to solidify this new awareness. Take some time to write down the memory or fantasy and especially the feelings that you've identified. One-by-one acknowledge each of the feelings - these are your Core Desires.

If the visualization didn't quite work for you, take a look at the long, but not exhaustive, list of feelings above and write a list of any of them that feel pertinent to your arousal. Once you have your list, rank them from most to least important. Pay attention to themes across the different words. For example, if you choose dissolved, united, and merged, you can see the way that all of these have a similar feel to them.

Fantasies are a Gold Mine

If you happen to fantasize, your fantasies are likely your most direct route to discovering the feelings you want to have. Whether they come from your imagination or you've picked them up from a movie, book, porn video, or erotic story, you have chosen which parts to focus on. You may have even embellished them with your own special flavor.

As we talked about in an earlier section, the longing for these feelings begins when we are quite young. If you think about it, it makes perfect sense. As a child, you do not get to choose the hand you are dealt. Adults are in charge of your life. Even the most well-meaning adults won't be able to perfectly attune and respond to you, and they definitely cannot provide for everything you need. Additionally, they have their own traumas and dramas going on, which may rob you of their attention or cause them to treat you poorly. However, as a young child, you can't just say, "Hey, mom and dad, you're going to need to do this differently" or "Hey guys, I'm packing up and moving out, things aren't working out for me here."

So, what can you do? You can fantasize. You can fantasize about all sorts of non-sexual solutions to these challenges. Sometimes you start to pair these solution-oriented fantasies with sexual arousal or masturbation. Over time, this creates the sexual desires that will stick with you for the rest of your life.

So, take a moment to write down your most common fantasies and get as detailed as possible. Make sure you focus on the parts of the fantasy that are most exciting and arousing to you. Then, again, see what feelings these fantasies give you. See if you can be extremely honest with yourself here. There can be a lot of shame or discomfort in these fantasies. Since our culture is so sex-negative, you may simply feel ashamed of having sexual fantasies at all. Additionally, there are some things that may cause you to have more shame around your fantasies than others might experience.

The Hottest Sex You've Ever Had

Speaking of the hottest sex you've ever had - this is the next best pathway to finding out what turns you on. If you didn't think of your hottest sexual experience (or one of your hottest sexual experiences) as part of your visualization, take some time to remember it now and write about it. Make sure you write down all the details that made it most exciting even if they don't seem overtly sexual. For example, it might have been the months of build-up before you ever even touched that created most of your arousal.

Anna's story is a wonderful illustration of one woman's hottest sexual experience:

Anna had a crush on her dance teacher. For months, she dressed up in her sexiest clothes and attended lessons. She flirted and danced with him every chance she got, even though she knew he was in a relationship. One day, after class, he invited her to come over for a glass of wine. She was so excited, she was shaking all over and could barely drive to his house. She watched him open a bottle of wine as he told her that he and his girlfriend were "taking a break."

She told us she didn't really care whether it was true or not; she knew she was going to take the chance to be with him whenever it arose. After they drank a few more sips, he put on some slow, sensual music and extended his hand to invite her to dance. He had a wall mirror in his apartment, which he used for private lessons. He spun her so that they were both facing the mirror and his arms were wrapped around her.

"I've been wanting to touch you like this for months," he whispered in her ear, "You are the sexiest woman I've ever seen." Her panties, which were already wet with anticipation, became soaked. They danced slowly, as he gently caressed her arms with his fingertips and continued to tell her how much he desired her. When he turned her around again, they kissed for the first time and she felt like their lips melted together. She said every second of their touching, kissing, and eventual lovemaking was perfect for her from beginning to end.

When we got to the bottom of her Core Desire, it was to feel irresistible. Some themes that accentuated this core desire were longing, her partner not able to resist cheating, and their mutual anticipation.

 Exercise:
Write Your Hottest Sexual Experience

If you like to write, this is the place to let your creative writer soar. Write your hottest sexual experience in as much detail as possible. Make sure you give time to explore the build-up, the tensions, the connection, the looks, sensations, and emotions you had and your partner (or partners) had during the experience. Then, see if you can get to the bottom of your Core Desires by seeing what that experience made you feel. Write down any feelings associated with your hottest sexual experience.

Other Pathways to Your Unique Core Desires

If you really don't have many fantasies and haven't had great sex, there are a number of other ways to discover your Core Desires.

The Stories That Tell All

One place to start is to think back on books you've read that have had sensual, romantic, erotic, or overtly sexual scenes. Write down any particular scenes that may have aroused you. It is a good idea to re-read these stories in order to see what, in particular, turned you on about them. You can also pick up a book of erotica.

For examples of women's most common fantasies, we often recommend the books written by Nancy Friday, including Women on Top and My Secret Garden. The great thing about these books is that they are based on Friday's research on actual women's fantasies, so they have many relatively well-written short fantasies that might ignite your erotic imagination. If you think you might be into BDSM, the Sleeping Beauty Quartet by Anne Rice (originally published under the nom de plume A. N. Roquelaure) is a great read.

If you pick up a more general book on erotica, don't despair if few or none of the stories turn you on. Because what arouses each person is so different, the first book you pick up may not touch on any of your Core Desires. If at first you don't succeed, pick up another book or check out an erotica website. Some of our clients have found stories that they like on Literotica.com. If any of the stories do get you turned on, take a minute to write down the actions that particularly turned you on. Then see if you can get to the bottom of the feelings you feel when you put yourself in the shoes of the different characters. See which feelings you relate to the most. If you are uncertain about what kinds of feelings you are looking for, we've included a list in the visualization exercise on page 40.

One of our clients said he was extremely turned on by comic books he read as a child. In a couple of them, there were stories about the heroes kissing or having sex with their cousins. He was very excited by the idea of his heroes, who society thought of as the "good guys," engaging in such taboo behavior. He felt like he was seen by everyone as a good kid, and no one had any idea how naughty his thoughts were. His excitement came from the idea of being naughty and secretive and getting away with it. All his adult fantasies were about doing naughty things while being seen as a nice guy.

Day Tripper - A One Way Ticket to Desire

Does your mind ever wander off during the day to intimate experiences you really hope will happen? Hints at the feelings you want to have can be found by digging into your daydreams. Whether they are overtly sexual or not is unimportant, just start to pay attention to what you think when you start to drift off. What arousing daydreams do you have? When you daydream about someone to whom you are attracted, what about them excites you? What kinds of thoughts get you turned on?

One of our clients, Angie, was always imagining being naked in nature. In her daydreams, she imagined herself walking through the forest naked on a hot day. She would stumble upon a warm rock. She pictured herself lying down on the rock. She felt the rock support her and the warmth spread across her ass and between her thighs. Her Core Desires were to be held and nourished.

When she saw herself as part of the natural world, she had the sense that the whole world was there to hold her and give her sustenance. This was in stark contrast to her childhood. Her parents were very neglectful and spent their time drinking and taking drugs. Through these fantasies of being a part of the natural world, Angie got the sense that nourishment was available and bountiful.

Until we started talking with Angie about it, she hadn't counted these daydreams as sexual. She had been dating a woman who had very overt sexual fantasies and felt something was wrong with her because she didn't see herself as sexual. You may also be someone whose Core Desires have more to do with nature. Your arousal might come from being in nature, smelling the damp earth, or perhaps feeling the sun on your body. Even though Angie's daydreams didn't seem sexual, they were actually the key to figuring out what she wanted for herself sexually.

From 50 Shades to the L Word

Media is a wonderful place to gather ideas about your turn-ons. Think about the times that you felt tingly, aroused, or excited by particular moments in movies or television. Remember, these moments may or may not have been overtly sexual. Are there sensual scenes from particular movies or TV shows that have always stuck with you? Even if you only get a tiny tingle from these scenes, write them down. Anything can be a clue.

Make sure you include arousing scenes that caused you to be surprised or embarrassed about the fact that they excited you. For example, many sexual fantasies have taboo or power dynamics in them so you may have been aroused by sexual interactions that you know you don't actually want to have in real life. That's just fine. Remember, you did not choose your sexual desires, but ignoring them may lead to a much less fulfilling sex life, and may even lead you to unconsciously act out in a way that could be harmful to yourself or others.

Aki and her husband came to us because they were having very little sex. They were trying to have a baby, but she confided in us that she was not at all attracted to her husband. She thought he was handsome, but he just didn't do it for her. He was too direct, she said. He would come home from work, never give her a kiss or embrace and then ask if she wanted to have sex later on. There was nothing sexy about his directness for her.

When asked what would do it for her, she asked if we'd ever seen the television show The Good Wife. After the session, she sent over some video clips of her favorite scenes from the show. The scenes were full of erotic tension between the main character, a married woman, and her lawyer associate. You could see the longing and desire in his eyes when he looked at her, and she finally reciprocated when the two embraced in a passionate kiss. Aki's Core Desires had everything to do with unspoken longing - a longing that was so powerful nothing else could get in the way of it. After a long build-up the longing was never spoken of, just passionately acted on. When the longing was finally acted upon, she also wanted to feel swept up, taken, and overwhelmed by her partner's desire for her.

 Exercise:
Learning from the Movies

Write down any scenes that turned you on and think about what feelings they inspire in you.

Are You Down With OPP - Other People's Pleasures?

You may have friends or relatives who talk about sex all the time. Whether or not you love to hear their stories, someone may have shared a story with you about a sexual experience they had that set your thoughts on fire. Think of any stories you've heard from the folks around you and see what you felt when they were telling them. Was it the content of the story that was arousing you? Did the excitement come from the fact that they were telling you these stories? See if you can identify and write down the feelings that were arousing in these stories or from these interactions.

One client we worked with, Axel, had a religious upbringing. He was very sheltered; however, he had an older step-sister on his father's side who was the black sheep of the family. She would come home for holiday dinners with a clear agenda to upset her father and step-mother. At the last family dinner, she started talking about a sex party she had attended where she had enjoyed herself by participating in a group sex scene.

Later that night, Axel's mind began to wander to his own group sex fantasy. It was the first time he allowed himself to acknowledge his bisexual desires. The fact that there was a woman in the scene gave him permission to imagine really enjoying sexual experiences with a man. As we dived deeper into the fantasy, he realized that having the woman there somehow let him move beyond his internalized homophobia to discover his Core Desires, which were feelings of togetherness and harmony. His parent's relationship was extremely discordant, but in his fantasies, everyone loved, cared for, and enjoyed giving pleasure to one another.

A Little Porn Goes a Long Way (And Yes, There Is Some Porn for Women)

We think of porn as the heroin of sex. It takes your brain right to your most intense arousal states, and can give you lots of clues about what you want to feel during sex. Thinking about what kinds of porn you watch, or watching it for the first time, can be a great way to learn about your Core Desires.

If You Watch Porn

If you already watch porn, you may have specific search terms that you use. Even within those search terms, you may also click around to find the scenes and the moments in the scenes that are most arousing. What are the real zingers for you? What is happening right before you are taken over the edge to orgasm? It might be the moment the nipples get caressed, or the cock slides in, or the slap across the ass. It might be the particular characters and their relationship, including age difference, power differences, differences in attractiveness, or familial relationship.

You can refer to the feelings list from the visualization and consider what feelings watching these scenes and actions ignite in you. There can be hints about the feelings you want to have in your search terms if you are using search terms like dominance, submission, or violation.

If You Don't Watch Porn

Navigating porn can be quite an endeavor. Before you even start your search, you may want some privacy so that people can't check your computer and see what websites you've visited. To keep your privacy, start by opening an incognito window. This way, the history of your porn searches won't show up in your browser so you can feel relaxed to try out different sites and rest assured that this adventure is just between you and your computer screen. When you finish watching, make sure you close the incognito window.

When browsing porn, some people have specific search terms that they punch into Google, while others go to porn video sharing sites like RedTube or PornHub, where porn of all kinds is compiled. These sites generally organize the videos into categories. One way to get an idea of what is exciting to you is to look over the list of categories that are included. Examples of categories that people browse or search are Lesbian, Threesome, MILF, and Bondage. See if any particular search terms pique your interest. You might also try clicking on the categories you don't usually go to and see if there is anything there that gets you going.

If you have never watched porn before, you may not want to dive right into the deep end of porn watching. Sometimes looking at these video sharing sites can bring up a lot of different kinds of images that you can't unsee. For this reason, you might consider looking into amateur porn sites or porn sites that are made specifically for women.

One of our favorite erotic film directors is Erika Lust. She has a very creative approach and does many different interesting projects. For one of these projects, Erika asked women to send in their sexual fantasies, and then hired actors to play out those fantasies on film. The wonderful thing about these movies is that they are already focused on specific women's desires so they can bring in more complex and interesting themes and acts.

When it comes to watching porn, it is easy to get confused and focus on sexual acts, but what really matters is to look for the feelings. For example, you might be very interested in anal sex. However, the underlying feeling that anal gives people can be quite different. For example, some givers of anal feel dominant, others feel received, others enjoy breaking taboos, and others feel something else entirely. For receivers of anal, it might be about feeling submissive, generous, adventurous, able to handle whatever is being dished out, masterful for being able to offer this kind of pleasure, or something completely different.

Ed's story is a good example of learning what turned him on about the porn he watched. Growing up, Ed's parents were both gorgeous and very materialistic. They were always putting on the perfect front out in the world. Yet, they'd come home and fight with each other, screaming and yelling late into the night. He felt like they hated each other and would have gotten a divorce if it wouldn't look so bad to others.

Ed loved amateur porn. Amateur porn is where real-life couples (or at least people pretending to be real-life couples) create their own homespun porn. He loved the way amateur porn was so real. He especially liked it when it was two average looking people in a dumpy bedroom who seemed to be really into each other and excited about what they were doing. Ed's Core Desires centered around feeling authentic, loving, and enthusiastic. If you'd like to check out some amateur porn, you might try makelovenotporn.tv. It's a site where real couples are having highly intimate sex.

 Exercise:
The Feelings You Get From Porn

Write down scenes that really turn you on and the feelings that go along with them.

While No News Is Good News - Some News Might Be Hot News

Even if you are not much of a media consumer, you may be someone who likes to read the news. Often news stories can have titillating aspects to them as there is often coverage of sex scandals or sex crimes. Check in to see if you are someone who is attracted to particular types of sexual stories in the news and pay attention to what the main themes of these stories are. Write down any stories that have gotten a rise out of you.

Paula was obsessed with reading stories about female teachers who had sex with their students. As a teenager herself, she had been quite beautiful but painfully shy and did not date at all in high school, finally having sex for the first time at 21. When she read the news stories, she would imagine herself in the role of a young, beautiful teacher who got to pick whichever high school senior she was most attracted to.

She would invite them to her classroom and have them sit in their desk chair. She would walk around them slowly, watching these young boys who were so confident with their peers suddenly become nervous and shaky as she asked them about their sexual experiences and fantasies. She could see them becoming more aroused and shifting in their seats as she started to stroke their hair and touch their bodies.

When they tried to touch her back, she would stop them, saying "Not yet." Slowly, she would put her hand between their legs. Sometimes she imagined them coming right away, unable to handle the intensity. Other times, she imagined rewarding the ones who held out by pulling their dick out of their jeans, pulling her panties aside, and sitting on it. Her Core Desires were to feel chosen and in charge.

 Exercise:
The Feelings You Get From the News

Write down the news stories that turned you on the most and the feelings that they elicited in you.

Now That You Know What You Want to Feel...

So far, you learned all about your Core Desires - what you want to feel from sex. Hopefully, you are beginning to get some insight into your sexual psyche and to better understand why certain sexual experiences or fantasies are so much hotter for you than others. Next, it's time to see where these desires came from and the different pathways to get to them.

Understanding Your Wounds Helps You Understand Your Core Desires

For as long as people have been trying to understand human behavior, theorists of psychology have looked at childhood development as a key to understanding how people behave throughout their lives. Since our social templates are shaped by early experiences in the family and with peers, our adult lives continue to be impacted by our childhood.

In particular, child development psychologists look at the key needs we have at different early ages, and what happens when these needs are met well or met poorly. If poorly met, we end up with woundings that automatically drive us towards meeting certain unfulfilled needs and forming particular protective strategies. In order to understand how this is connected to your Core Desires, it is important to know how your sexual desires were formed.

By necessity, humans are social creatures, meaning we need other humans to survive. In order to invest in a large frontal cortex, birth needed to happen before we were fully formed, necessitating a long period of dependency on our parents and caregivers. Even after we are no longer dependent on our parents, we are dependent on our community for our survival. In a perfect (and non-existent) world, our caregivers would be able to attune to us and respond to our needs perfectly. However, each child's needs are different, and each parent also has their own historical wounds that make it impossible to achieve perfect parenting.

During our development, each of us experienced unfulfilled needs and painful challenges, which resulted in us having certain core wounds. An example of a core wound might be feeling like you don't matter, or feeling like no one understands or accepts you. Our strategies of dealing with these wounds help the large majority of us stay psychologically intact so we can become functional adults in the world. Part of the way that we maintain our psychological well-being is through fantasies. One way that people soothe themselves is by longing and fantasizing that their experiences were different or by replaying the challenging experiences but seeing themselves as having some kind of control over the situation.

Many of these soothing fantasies of fulfillment or re-enactment are non-sexual daydreams. They can vary from nurture-oriented fantasies like being cared for and loved to violent fantasies of justice or retribution. Others take on a more sexual nature, and eventually, we begin masturbating while thinking about them. This allows us to transform painful experiences into experiences of pleasure.

And, these soothing fantasies are ultimately part of what shapes what we long for in our sexual lives. In other words, our sexual fantasies that developed as an attempt to deal with old wounds or attain unmet needs, motivate us to seek out particular kinds of erotic experiences.

The Two Different Pathways to Our Core Desires

Two different pathways lead to the attainment of our Core Desires. The first is what we call The Resolution Pathway, the second, we refer to as The Repetition with Agency Pathway.

Pathway 1: The Resolution Pathway

The Resolution Pathway is when we fantasize about and act out desires that soothe the unmet needs by giving us the positive experiences that contrast with the painful ones we had in childhood. In other words, if we were ignored as a child, our Core Desires might be to feel very seen or cared for. This gives us a feeling of the hurt being resolved - thus the Resolution Pathway.

If you recall the stories of Mary, who wanted to be seen, and Bill, who wanted to be adored, you can see that the Core Desires that developed from these experiences were very straightforward attempts to emotionally soothe the childhood feeling of unworthiness. They developed Core Desires that were a positive resolution to the unfulfilled need for a sense of worth. Both Bill's and Mary's fantasies offered the opposite of the negative experiences they had in their childhood.

We call this a Resolution Pathway because it is a desire to get the opposite experience than the one they had as a child. Both Bill and Mary wanted to feel worthy of attention and affection. In this case, the Resolution Pathway is directed at the need for worth and the wound of feeling unworthy. The Resolution Fantasy acts as a balm that soothes the feeling of being unwanted and helps them feel their sense of worth in the world.

Here are some other common woundings and their possible corresponding Resolution Pathways:

❖ Feeling unsafe - creating a scene in which your partner snuggles you up tightly (maybe after watching a scary movie) goes at your pace, asks you what you need, and tells you "you're safe here."

❖ Being neglected and not cared for - being taken out to a nice hotel and pampered with attention and nurturing touch, and having your needs anticipated.

❖ Having to do a lot on your own - allowing a partner to be dominant and tell you exactly what to do so that you don't have to be responsible.

❖ Feeling that you are not free and have no choice - walking and dancing around the house nude, eventually having sex in a random location in the house (or outside in a backyard or on a deck).

❖ Feeling humiliated - being the dominant person who is powerful and calling all the shots in the sexual experience.

Pathway 2: Repetition With Agency Pathway

The Repetition with Agency pathway is when the person's Core Desires are a repetition of the hurt, but the person re-enacts the painful experience with a sense of control over it. In the Repetition with Agency Pathway, the person is soothing the wound by consciously choosing to engage in the repetition instead of the hurt happening to them without their control over when and how it happens.

We find Repetition with Agency to be a less understood pathway that is often judged and frowned upon. When people have a Repetition with Agency pathway, they may feel ashamed and want to hide it, and well-intentioned helpers may try to get them to change it. However, these fantasies may be a person's most efficient and effective route to arousal and are not inherently harmful.

If a person is consciously choosing to embrace and engage in this pathway, that is an empowered choice. It is just as possible that Bill and Mary's fantasies might have been repetition fantasies. A repetition fantasy could be that their lover withholds touch, kisses, and affection, making them beg for it. The feeling of not getting what they want would create intense arousal.

By engaging in Repetition with Agency experiences, a person incorporates the painful experiences that they had as a child into arousal and pleasure. This previously painful experience is part of their sexual fulfillment, changing it from a net negative to a net positive outcome, especially if they can get rid of any shame they have for wanting to engage in it.

Here are some other common woundings and their corresponding Repetition with Agency Pathways:

- ❖ Feeling abandoned - imaging your partner having sex with someone else (or even carrying that fantasy out).

- ❖ Feeling unsafe - being blindfolded and tied up and not knowing what will happen next.

- ❖ Experiencing a lack of care - finding a partner that can feign (role-play) disinterest or dissatisfaction and aloofness.

- ❖ Shame - putting on a collar and being walked around the home like a pet or someone subservient, being called degrading names.

The agency part of Repetition with Agency means that you have a sense of your Core Desires and are going after them consciously. You might be negotiating them with a partner or not, but you know what you are doing and why. Repetition with Agency needs to be contrasted with folks who are doing repetition without any sense of self-awareness or agency. Repetition without agency would be going after something that is familiar but does not feel good at all, or that feels good in the moment, but the aftermath - what we call a shame-over - is so bad that the sum total of the behavior is making your life worse, not better.

An example of repetition without agency would be going after a partner over and over again who you feel hurt and rejected by. You may experience the highs and the arousal of getting them to be with you in the moment you do connect, but you feel debilitated by the experience afterward and are constantly distracted and obsessed by wanting something that is not actually available to you. Moving from unconscious repetition to Repetition with Agency is a process that we help many clients go through in coaching so that they can get the yummy parts of their Core Desires met without all of the negative fallout.

Either Pathway – Resolution or Repetition With Agency – Is Great

Whether your Core Desires follow the pathway of Resolution or Repetition with Agency, or a combination of the two, embracing them and learning how to get them met out in the world safely and consensually can be a hugely liberating experience. Seeking out and/or engaging with these erotic experiences allows people to create a different relationship with their wounds and can result in healing.

The healing comes from lowering shame as well as getting the positive experience or taking control over the hurt. When you get these Core Desires celebrated and met over and over again, the sting of the old wounds lowers, and you become more resilient and confident.

How (And Whether) to Share Your Core Desires

One of the most deeply vulnerable and scary things you can do is share the contents of your erotic imagination with your partner. This may be the first time you are really trying to articulate what you want, and you may feel like you don't quite have the words to describe it, or you might feel embarrassed saying it. You might be afraid to feel judged or shamed, or you might have already tried to communicate about it with your past or current partner and felt rejected or shut down.

Sharing your Core Desires can be an amazing opportunity to deepen intimacy in your relationship. It can be very empowering to fully own and share who you are with your partner and sharing your Core Desires is the most likely route to you having the hottest sex over the long term.

At the same time, as there are many wonderful reasons to share your Core Desires, there can also be some potential challenges.

There are instances where sharing your Core Desires with a partner could be detrimental to your partnership, and we don't want to downplay this. If your Core Desires are something you feel may be threatening to your partner or that they might find it repulsive, you have to check with yourself if you are ready to deal with all of the potential consequences of sharing, including your partner judging, distancing from, or even leaving you.

Your partner may also "out you" by sharing this information with other people that you know. Additionally, if you share custody of a child with your partner, you could be taking a risk sharing your Core Desires in that they may use it in a custody battle to say that you are an unfit parent. While these outcomes are rare, we feel it is important to mention them so that you can make a fully informed decision about whether and with whom to share your Core Desires. Ultimately, you will need to decide whether or not you feel safe enough to share.

If you do decide to share and if your relationship is in a good place, you can simply follow the steps below. If you have already been fighting about sex, it is important to start the conversation by letting your partner know that you have learned new things about yourself that you didn't fully understand before, and that you'd like to have the conversation in a different way. The best way to approach sharing is to think of it as a way to deepen intimacy and to avoid pressure for any particular outcomes.

For example, you might say "I know I have been pushing for (fill in the blank here) and it must have been painful to feel all this pressure from me. I can imagine you have felt (fill in the feeling here - afraid or like you aren't enough or frustrated and hurt that you aren't meeting my needs). I've recently spent some time reading and understanding myself more deeply and I want to have a conversation between us that doesn't feel like the old, painful conversations we've been having. The goal isn't for me to get every fantasy fulfilled, but for us to understand each other better and feel more connected. After I share about myself, I'd also like to hear more about you."

In order to have successful conversations about your Core Desires, there are some very important guidelines we recommend you follow. This conversation begins (Step 1) with one partner sharing what they have learned about themselves from Coming Together so far. It's best to start with sharing what you deeply want to feel. Step 2 and 3 are for partner 2 and are about how to listen and celebrate while still keeping your boundaries. Once you've done it in one direction, you will need to switch and have the conversation in the other direction as well.

Step 1: Partner 1 Tell Partner 2 What You Want to **Feel** First

Instead of starting the conversation with what you want to do with your partner, start by telling them more generically about what you want to feel from sex. In this way, you depersonalize your Core Desires a bit and make it easier for them to hear your desires without feeling like it is their job to meet all of them. Additionally, talking about what you want to *feel* as opposed to what you want to *do* is much more likely to create empathy in your partner as opposed to creating fear.

For example, if you say, "When I was a child, I really felt like my parents didn't want me, so I realize that all my fantasies really come back to me feeling like I'm deeply and irresistibly desirable." This is really different than saying, "I've been thinking I want to go to a sex party and find other men or women for us to have sex with." While you might have the fantasy that going to a sex party will give you the feeling you want to have (and it might), there may be other ways to get that feeling and it will be helpful for your partner to understand the underlying need so that they are less likely to get scared and therefore judge and shame your desires.

If your Core Desires feel like they are less common, more likely to be judged, or more on the kinky side, it can be helpful to test the waters around how open a partner might be. We suggest, before you go into the specifics of your Core Desires, you ask a question like, "Are you kink-friendly?" or "Are you open to trying out different kinds of sexual experiences?" This is likely to get you into a conversation where you can gauge how open your partner might be to hearing about your Core Desires.

Step 2: Partner 2 Celebrate - Don't Judge

When you are sharing your Core Desires, you are inviting the possibility of the deepest and most healing experience of acceptance. You are also taking a big risk. Our society is full of many judgments about what kind of sex is "good," "healthy," and "appropriate," yet almost all of us have some desires or thoughts that lie outside those narrow bounds.

Your and your partner's desires are beautiful expressions of the deepest parts of who you are. Some of these desires will be played out in your life together and some will not. You will want to experience some desires, while others you will want to keep in the realm of fantasy. Regardless, when your partner is sharing their deepest erotic desires, they are giving you a tremendous gift of trust and intimacy. When you receive them as such and celebrate the beauty of these desires, it is a wonderful opportunity to make your bond even more solid.

Step 3: Partner 2 Listen Without Going Into Obligation

People often judge their partner's desires and fantasies because they are afraid that it is their job to meet all of their partner's desires. You might feel obligated to fulfill your partner's desires or threatened by them because you can't or don't want to fulfill them. These fears may make you wish some of your partner's desires didn't exist. It is much easier to fully accept your partner's desires without judgment if you remember that desires do not necessarily have to happen. It is not your job to do anything you don't want to do.

When you are listening to your partner's Core Desires, listen with the feeling that you are deepening intimacy by better understanding them. Learning more about your partner, and accepting them for who they are, is a big part of what makes relationships sustainable. Before you even think about having to take any actions, see if you can empathize with what your partner wants to feel. Instead of feeling obligated to fulfill those desires, take time to celebrate them knowing you always have a right to your boundaries. **Make sure you both get a turn!**

We hope this process of discovering your Core Desires and sharing them has already begun to help you understand and articulate your erotic nature. It has helped our clients have astoundingly positive shifts in their desire, arousal, pleasure, and connection. Now that you have an idea of your Core Desires, it is time to figure out how you want to experience them out in the world. We call the experience of acting out your Core Desires in the most exciting ways your Hottest Sexual Movies.

Part II

Experience Your Hottest Sexual Movie

Your Hottest Sexual Movie

Nearly everyone walks in the world with one or more sexual "movies"—images and ideas of how they want sex to look, and what kind of experiences they want to play out. We call these your Hottest Sexual Movies and they are the most surefire way to get to your Core Desires. Usually, people have one or a few very specific Hottest Sexual Movies that are the most direct pathway to giving them their Core Desires.

While you may have the ability to enjoy multiple forms of seduction, the closer you are to getting your exact Hottest Sexual Movie, the more pleasurable and intense sex will be. If the idea that you have one or a few Hottest Sexual Movies does not resonate for you, your Core Desire might be freedom, novelty, creativity, or something in that vein. If your deepest sexual need is to feel free or for things to feel creative or new, your Hottest Sexual Movie will require constant innovation.

The Same Core Desires Can Lead to Different Hottest Sexual Movies

One person's Core Desires might require a completely different Hottest Sexual Movie than another's. If you want to feel special, there are probably very specific Hottest Sexual Movies that will give you that feeling of specialness, and they will be different from another person's pathway to specialness. A romantic experience might be your pathway to feeling special while an experience of dominance and submission might be another person's. Take the following examples:

Romance as a Pathway to Feeling Special

Your partner rings the doorbell and, when you answer, they are standing at the door with your favorite wine and a single long stem rose. This makes you feel special because they have paid attention to you enough to know that you love this particular cabernet and that roses are your favorite flower. Once you've put the flower in water and you are standing with the freshly-poured wine in your hand, they pause in the middle of a sentence and look deeply into your eyes, "When you smile like that, I lose my ability to think and now I've completely forgotten what I was about to say." You feel special because they are so overwhelmed with feelings for you, that they are speechless. They lean over and kiss your lips softly, caressing your cheek with their hand. The slowness and care with which they kiss and touch you lets you know that you are so special that they want to take their time with you.

Dominance and Submission as a Pathway to Feeling Special

Imagine that your partner has spent the whole day preparing to give you this experience. They have found the perfect hotel room near your favorite restaurant and paid close attention to the desires that you previously expressed.

When you arrive at the restaurant and sit down, you find that you do not have to do anything, your partner has already ordered your favorite meal and it comes to you in courses. You are told you have to keep your hands on your lap as they feed you each bite, making sure you don't get too full to take all the pleasure that is about to come. You feel special because they are taking exquisite care of you, and are fully attentive and attuned to your needs.

Their attention to your every wish continues when you return to the hotel. They have purchased fur-lined cuffs, telling you they know how delicate your skin is and how precious you are. They check on you as they tie you down, making sure that you are ok before they slowly begin to slide pieces of your favorite fruits and dark chocolates across your mouth and lips. This makes you feel special because they are so attentive.

They take time with every inch of your body, paying close attention to your most erogenous zones. They know that you cannot resist it when they lick their tongue on the outside of your armpit. They take time to admire the goosebumps running down your arm, then, looking in your eyes, they tell you, "I've never wanted to possess anyone the way I want to possess you." This makes you feel special because they know your body and want you more than anyone else.

The Same Hottest Sexual Movie Can Lead to Different Core Desires

One person's Hottest Sexual Movie that makes them feel special might make another person feel something completely different. The above Hottest Sexual Movies could potentially meet the needs of people with many different Core Desires. For example, the romantic scene could make you feel loved, precious, and/or seen. The dominant/submissive scene could make you feel possessed, taken care of, attuned to, and/or adored. The exact same movie can be very satisfying for many different underlying Core Desires.

This is why, whenever anyone tells us a Hottest Sexual Movie, we always try to figure out their Core Desires as well - the feelings that they get from these experiences. For example, a person may have a spanking fantasy because they like the feeling of punishing someone. A spanking fantasy could also point to a desire to have a very intense and present connection. Nothing brings someone into the present moment like a good, hard spanking.

If you tell your partner that you are interested in a particular sex act, that is not necessarily enough information for them to give you one of your Hottest Sexual Movies because they won't know what feelings you want to feel or the best way to get you there. This is because the same exact acts can be done in many different ways and with many different attitudes.

The Many Faces of a Threesome

Let's take the example of a threesome. Many people have threesome fantasies, but one person's reason for wanting a threesome may be quite different from someone else's. As you read through the examples of the different feelings people can get from having a threesome, imagine what kind of experiences a person might have had in their childhood that could potentially lead to these Core Desires.

1. **Teamwork** - A person might want to feel like they are on a team with their partner, picking up a third, seducing them, and driving them wild all night long.

2. **Compersion** - Compersion is a word created by the polyamorous community. The definition is taking pleasure in the fact that someone you love is getting pleasure from someone else. One person in a couple may want to feel compersion by seeing their partner enjoying pleasure, kissing, and receiving orgasms from another person.

3. **Not Responsible** - One person in a couple may want to feel free from the hard work and responsibility of always having to please their partner. They may want to do very little, mostly sitting back and watching the action.

4. **Desired and Adored** - A person might want to feel like they are the king or queen receiving all of the attention, pleasure, and adoration of two people waiting on them and fulfilling their every sexual need.

5. **Freedom** - A single person may want to have sex with a couple so that they don't have to worry about getting into any kind of emotional entanglement. They come, enjoy the experience, then skip off into the sunset by themselves, leaving the couple to process any feelings about the experience with each other.

6. **Etc., etc., etc.** - Maybe you have a threesome fantasy that is something different like the feeling that love is infinite or enjoying being the boss of not just one but two people, or being watched (exhibitionism). The possibilities are endless.

Let's say that you and your partner both agree that you are interested in having a threesome. Now that you know that there are so many different potential motives for a threesome, you can see that just agreeing you both want one doesn't mean you are interested in the same kind of threesome. If you don't talk with your partner about what feelings you are trying to create (Your Core Desires), and how you want to create them (Your Hottest Sexual Movies), you may go into the experience with very different desires and expectations. We will talk much more about compatibility across differing Core Desires and Hottest Sexual Movies in Part III. But first, let's talk about how to talk about your movie.

How to Talk About Your Hottest Sexual Movie

In order to create the sex life you want, you will need to talk about your Hottest Sexual Movie (or Movies) as well as teach them. It is great to separate this into two different steps. The first step is to tell the story of your movie. A story is a narrative of what you might like to happen during an erotic experience. For example, a romantic story will be about love, while passion is more about uncontrollable desires.

You don't need to have a perfectly coherent story with a beginning, a middle, and an end. It might be more like little snippets or ideas of experiences you want to have. For example, "I want us to take a romantic ride together up to a beautiful vista and just look at each other and flirt, building tension before we even kiss," could be the whole story. The more depth, details, and snippets you can offer, the more your partner will learn about what you want.

To Personalize or Not to Personalize

When it comes to sharing your Hottest Sexual Movie with your partner, you will want to ask them whether they would rather hear you talk about what you want to do with them or whether they'd rather have you share it generically. For some people, hearing it generically will be better because it will take the pressure off of them having to fulfill everything or from feeling like they have to do it just exactly right for you. For others, they will want to hear you talk about your desires with them because a generic description would be too impersonal.

An example of sharing it generically would be to say, "In my Hottest Sexual Movie, my lover would..." An example of sharing it personally would be to say, "In my Hottest Sexual Movie, you would..."

If your partner wants you to share it personally, it is extremely important that you focus on what you want them to do or not do without any kind of criticism of past experiences. For example, your partner is likely to get very defensive if you say something like "I'd really like you to kiss me all over my body, but I don't want you to focus on my breasts right away like you always do." To avoid pressure and criticism, try to paint a picture for your partner of your ideal experience going forward instead of dwelling on the past. You might instead say, "I'd love for you to kiss me all over my body, giving equal attention to all of my parts."

Give as Many Details as Possible

The more you tell your partner about what you want, the better. You can give them specifics on what you want to happen during your day-to-day experiences together that will help keep you in the mood when you are not feeling sexual. You can help them understand how you want to be approached and what attitude you'd like them to bring. For example, you might want to start with more playfulness or for them to take their desire for you very seriously.

It can be helpful to offer your partner specific words or phrases that are the most arousing to you, as well as those that are off-limits because they bring your arousal down or feel offensive to you. For example, we had one client who loved being called a slut but hated being called a whore. We had another client who had a list of words and phrases that they found most arousing and they would send this list to their partner over email.

You can also let your partner know how you want to be touched - more firmly or more feathery or both. Even giving them an idea of how you want to be looked at can be wonderful. You can let them know where you want to have sex - the bedroom, dining room, or forest - and what time of day you are most aroused.

Here's a great example of some clients describing their Hottest Sexual Movies to their partner. This first one is a man whose Core Desire is to feel *taken care of*.

"I imagine I come to your house one evening and you are wearing this very sexy outfit. You know I will like it because it is almost exactly like an outfit we had seen in a movie we watched the week before. I told you I liked it but wasn't really sure if you were paying attention to what I said. When I walk through the door, you tell me that I don't need to do anything for you this evening, that tonight is completely about me. You say I should sit down on the couch. This is when I know I will feel my whole body relax because I know you have decided to take full care of me tonight.

"You begin unbuttoning my shirt. You get behind me and start rubbing my shoulders, and your hands go to each place of tension with just the right pressure. Then, you come around in front of me and kiss my mouth and start kissing down my chest. You go slowly, teasing me on the way down so I can feel the build-up as you move down my chest to my stomach.

"You undo my belt and unzip my pants, pulling them off so I can make myself comfortable. You put a pillow down between my feet and kneel in front of me. You start licking the head of my dick and looking up at me. I feel like you are watching my responses so that you can gauge my arousal and play with me, bringing me up and down. As you continue to lick and suck, you cup and rub my balls with your hand. I feel like you are reading every little response and anticipating the next move I want.

"The hottest part for me would be if you would encourage me to come in your mouth by saying something like, 'I want to taste your cum' or 'I want your cum inside of me.' Then, when I come in your mouth, if some of it drips down the sides of my dick, you lick it up like you can't get enough, leaving me all nice and clean and completely satisfied."

Here's another example from a woman who likes to feel like *she doesn't have to be responsible* for her partner's pleasure, but she can join in if she wants.

"I imagine my partner and I are home on a Saturday and maybe I'm doing some extra work that I didn't have time to do during the week. My partner says to me, 'I'm going to go to the bedroom and masturbate. Feel free to join me if you'd like.' I feel absolutely no pressure to join then because I know that they can fully take care of themselves. As I sit and work, my thoughts occasionally wander to images of my partner touching themselves. I imagine they are watching the porn that turns them on the most and I start to feel myself get a little wet thinking about it. I imagine their arousal going up and I feel my arousal going up as well.

"I finish my work in a relaxed way and go to the bedroom to see if they are still enjoying themselves. If they are, I will ask them if it's ok for me to watch and join in if I feel like it. I love watching them turn themselves on and I start to touch myself at the same time. Then I move closer and we begin to touch each other, sharing the arousal we've each built inside of ourselves."

The most common Hottest Sexual Movies we hear from women are about romance. Here's an example of a romantic Hottest Sexual Movie:

"I want to be everything to you. I want to be the most beautiful, precious, and amazing woman you have ever seen. What feels most romantic to me is to feel like you only have eyes for me and that every other woman pales in comparison. It's not like I'm living a dream world - I realize that it's normal to be attracted to other people, but I really want to feel that feeling from you. I want to see it in your eyes when you look at me - I want to see how much you love me and how your heart beats faster when I'm around."

"I think the words I want to hear are, 'You are my everything.' It's funny, I keep wanting to make a caveat like I know that there are other parts of you, that you have your job and your hobbies, but it's not really about that. It is the feeling that when you are with me, you feel this adoration and when you are away from me, I am always on your mind. Like, I would love it if you left me a sweet note on my pillow that I find when I go upstairs to go to bed or if you are out and you happen to see a beautiful pair of earrings I would love and you bring them home to me."

"When it comes to having sex, I also love it when you start by looking in my eyes. Then I imagine you looking at my lips like you are longing to kiss them, but you wait because you can't decide which you want more, to look at me or to lean in and kiss me. Your words are so important too. When you tell me how much I mean to you, or that you love me, or that I'm your sweetness, it just makes me want to fall into you and share every part of myself. I love having my face stroked and my hair touched, and especially when you look at me and smile while shaking your head. I imagine you are saying to yourself, 'How did I find such an amazing woman?'"

"I love to be touched softly all over my body and I love to touch you too, your shoulders and arms. I think of them wrapped around me as I'm touching you and I feel the safety of your love and tenderness. I guess those are the main things... and kissing you, of course; there is hardly anything I like better than your kisses."

Some Movies We've "Watched"

We are firm believers in the idea that, in order to deeply understand yourself sexually or expand your repertoire, you need to know what's on the menu and how to ask for it. Many times couples come into our office and one or both of them are at a loss as to what really turns them on. They ask for ideas of where they can go to find more examples, and unfortunately, we've found that resources are limited.

In addition to all of the stories you've already read in the book so far, the following are more great examples of Core Desires and Hottest Sexual Movies that we've heard from our clients as well as ways you could communicate these Hottest Sexual Movies in a sensual and inviting way if you want them for yourself. Of course, your Core Desires and Hottest Sexual Movies will be unique to you. We are offering these as sample Hottest Sexual Movies and conversations to stroke your imagination and get your communication rolling. We've titled them with the Core Desires each of them wanted to get out of the experience.

Safe and Enveloped

We had one client, Margot, whose fantasies were all about connecting with water. In this fantasy, she was seeking out a safe place where she could experience a sense of *serenity*, *ease*, and arousal in her body.

It is a beautiful, warm day and I'm surrounded by hills as far as the eye can see. There is a creek flowing down a hill and through the valley that I'm in and it is refreshing but not too cold. I'm halfway submerged in the stream and I can feel the sun on my body as the water moves along my skin. I feel my back supported by the large, smooth rock I'm lying on and the water feels like a lover, caressing my hips and thighs, surrounding my nipples, rushing across my clitoris and labia.

I can feel that I am part of this natural world and that my arousal is as natural as the butterfly flying by. I scoop up some water and pour it across different parts of my body; it is clean enough to drink so I let it fill my mouth. Then I'm stroking my body along with the water. I stroke my wet, flowing hair. I stroke my breasts and nipples, down across my hips. I stroke my thighs as the water flows across them. I can feel my yoni opening like a flower and filling with water as I start touching my clitoris softly in the same way the water is, teasing myself slowly. I allow my body to follow its natural rhythms and I can feel my hips moving with the water. I know that my orgasm will come as naturally as the water flowing if I just keep allowing.

If your Core Desires are to feel *safe* and *enveloped* and Your Hottest Sexual Movies usually have water in them, you could ask your partner to begin foreplay in your bathtub or shower. You might say:

"Lover, it would turn me on so much if you would draw a hot bath for me and add some essential oils that I keep in the bathroom cabinet. My favorite right now is lavender."

"I would also appreciate any additions you could make to the environment, like lighting candles if it's nighttime or putting on some audio of running water. You could even add flower petals to the bath, they are so soft and they feel good on my skin. Once I'm in the bath, I'd love it if you would sit down next to the bath and start to caress my arms and belly. You could even use the flower petals - covering your fingertips with them and using them to bring softness to the caress. I can show you what I mean."

"It would be amazing if you had a cup you could use to pour water over my hair and back; whatever parts of my body are outside of the water. Then you could start to tease my breasts and nipples and tease my legs and thighs. I especially like my inner thighs teased. You could pour cups of water from a little bit of height over my yoni so I can feel the movement of the water flowing across my lips and clit. You can also stroke my outer lips with your fingertips or tease very lightly across my clit."

"If I get really aroused in the bath and want to keep going to orgasm, I have some special silicone lube that is waterproof. Please use it when you are giving more firm touch to my clit or going inside of me. If I'm not ready for an orgasm in the bath, I will stand up and then you can wrap a towel around me and guide me or carry me to the bed. We can have some towels down on the bed so you don't have to dry me off completely and I can feel the coolness of the water on my skin as we touch, kiss, and breathe together while we are making love."

Impactful

Jim described the best sexual experience of his life.

I was sitting across the bed from this woman I dated for a while and we were gazing into each other's eyes. We were both breathing deeply and it started to feel like we were breathing each other in. As we breathed, I began to see this glowing energy surround and connect us. I kept looking at her and her body began to rock with pleasure.

I didn't even need to touch her, her face started to flush and I was sending energy over to her. I was moving the energy through each of her chakras really slowly. Every time it moved to the next chakra, her body responded even though we never touched. Then she just started twitching and shaking all over. She told me afterward that she was having an energetic orgasm the whole time she was shaking. She didn't have to tell me because I felt the reverberations in my body too. I know my wife wants me to throw her down on the bed and have my way with her, but I actually was much more aroused and fulfilled by the energetic experiences I had with my ex.

If your Core Desire is to feel *impactful* and your Hottest Sexual Movies are very energetically based, you might say to your partner:

"What I want more than anything is for you to allow yourself to take in my sexual energy and let it connect with the sexual energy inside of your body. I can guide you through it with my words. You can picture the energy as light or colors and let yourself feel the strength of it moving in your body when I look at you.

"It can really help if you take deep breaths and pay attention to where I am looking at you, that is where I will be sending the energy. If I look in your eyes, it means I am sending it throughout your whole body. As you feel the energy moving more and more strongly inside of you, I will come closer, but I won't touch you right away. I will use my hands right near your skin to connect with the energy inside of you as we breathe together. Even though I'm not touching you, you will feel me throughout your body.

"I want you to let go and surrender to my energy. Your breath might get fast, you might feel different sensations in your body or you might find your body shaking. Feel free to let all of those responses happen. Let your body move or make sound or flow orgasmic energy through it."

Independent and Compersive (Joyful From Seeing Your Lover Receive Pleasure From Someone Else)

Kimberly came in with her wife, Angela, for couples' sessions and they were looking to open their relationship. Kimberly felt that Angela had a lot of needs from her and she wanted Angela to take responsibility for those needs. She didn't want to feel like it was her job to give Angela everything she needed.

I'm sitting on a chair in the bedroom watching my partner with her new lover. I have my vibrator nearby in case I need it. My partner is full of desires and she is asking her new lover for everything she wants. Her new lover is a man and he is very excited to give her everything. I am so pleased to see that she is being taken care of and I don't have to be the one to do it. I feel good that I have given her the independence and space she needs to get everything she wants.

As I sit and watch I feel relaxed and aroused. I am turned on by her pleasure and especially get off on the moments when she is very clear about what she needs. I use my vibrator to come, but I do it quietly because I do not want the attention on me. While it is arousing, and I'm happy to be a part of it, I also realize I would be just as happy going out to a nearby cafe and imagining my wife getting all of her needs met. It is not important that I'm there, only that I know she is fully taking care of herself and getting all filled up (no pun intended).

If your Core Desires are to feel independent and compersive and your Hottest Sexual Movie is about your partner being able to get their needs met while you watch (or not), you might say to your partner, "I love giving you pleasure so much, and I also really love the idea of you getting pleasure from another person. If it's ok with you, I'd love for us to find another lover for you. I'd be delighted to be there with you and watch or to not be there.

"What turns me on most about it, is the idea that you really know what you like and that you communicate that to your lover. It would be exciting for me to be a part of that communication. For example, if you were meeting someone online, I would love to be able to see a chat exchange where you tell them exactly what you want from them. Or, if you are talking on the phone with them, I'd love to be able to listen while you tell them exactly what you want them to do to you. Also, if you are open to sharing about your experiences during times that you meet with another lover and I'm not there, I'd love to hear any stories about how you asked for exactly what you needed and your other lover gave it to you."

On The Same Team and Naughty

A student of ours, Evan, described an experience that he had with his boyfriend.

From the very beginning, Lamar and I identified ourselves as partners in crime. I really love having elaborate sexual adventures. Prior to dating Lamar, I was always the one who was planning them out and offering the new ideas and experiences, so I was extremely surprised when I realized not only was Lamar totally on board with an adventurous sex life, he was also totally willing and, more importantly, able to co-create those experiences with me.

One day, I came to him and said, I really want to have sex in public. For me, there was nothing particularly exciting about being caught or watched, I just knew it was going to take some planning and that my partner in crime was going to help me get as creative and sneaky as we needed to. To be clear, I was not talking about having sex at some sex party with a bunch of other gay guys, we could do that any day of the week. I wanted to do it somewhere where we would be being very transgressive.

It turned into this two-month game, where we each kept coming up with more fun and outrageous places to screw. We did a hotel lobby in a fancy hotel, a vineyard at a Napa winery, an airport bathroom (it helped we were both men, of course). My very favorite was behind some trees on the old Apple campus, where I used to work. I loved that he came up with that one and took the time to scout it out. He had planned out exactly where we should park, the time of day, and the line of trees in mind. I almost couldn't stop laughing long enough to really suck his dick right. I had this feeling of glee that we were totally on this team together.

If your Core Desires are to feel on the same team and naughty, you can see a bit how Evan and Lamar negotiated it. Through the Somatica Core Training, Evan learned to be even more specific about sharing the feelings that he got from these adventures together. In this way, they were able to come up with many other scenarios that elicited those feelings. For example, they liked to go to a party and both flirt with the same person until they could tell there was a chance for a threesome, then the two of them would go home together and fantasize aloud while they had sex.

If this was your desire, you might ask for it by saying, "Babe, I love it when we come up with sexy plots and schemes together. I was thinking we could get all dressed up and go out together somewhere where we can check people out. I want us to talk about who we think is sexy and what we'd want to do to them once we got them home into our bed. If we find someone we are both attracted to, it would be awesome for us to flirt with them and see if we can get them to flirt back. At any point, one of us can give the secret signal we agree upon, which means it's time to go. Then, I want us to go home together and have sex while we tell each other stories about how we would team up on them."

Accepted and Desired

Analisa had body image issues that got in the way of her sexual arousal.

I have the most amazing lover in the world; he is perfect for me because in his eyes I am perfection. I spent so much time in my life evaluating myself and pushing myself to be better, but I don't have to do any of that for him. Actually, for him, I don't have to do anything at all. What he wants to do more than anything is delight in every inch of my body.

He undresses me and checks me out, tells me how sexy I am and how he loves every part of my body, the bounce in my breasts, the curves of my belly. He kisses me and, with his body heat, he warms the bed for me. He is fully in-tune and very contained with his energy, which gives me so much space and freedom to be myself.

I lie down and he looks at my body, enjoying me, telling me that he has been fantasizing about me all the time. He tells me that he wants to dive into me and that he is attracted by my unique beauty. He says when he thinks about who I am as a person and my body, he can't get his hand off himself, that I leave him shaking to a point that he can't come – that's how intensely he delights in everything about me.

He is caressing me, lightly and then more passionately, knowing exactly what feels good, responding with delight to every response that I offer. Later when I am coming endlessly he is in awe and fully desiring of my orgasms, my ejaculations, my moans. What turns me on the most is that feeling that he wants and accepts all of me exactly the way I am, with no changes – he makes me feel like I am his drug and who I am is the exact things that he wants and needs.

If your Core Desires are to feel accepted and desired and your Hottest Sexual Movie is to have your partner delight in every inch of you, you might say, "I want you to take your time with my body. I want you to look at and touch my body with a sense of awe and adoration. I want to feel like I can be myself completely and that you will keep touching me and licking me while taking enjoyment from all of my responses. Whether I am crying or squirting, I want you to stay with me and to not stop fucking me no matter what. I also want to hear you tell me how you feel about me, how it feels to be with me, and all the parts of me that you can't get enough of."

Mutually Vulnerable

One of our clients shared a transcendent experience she had.

When he looked in my eyes, I saw that he was completely open to me in a way I had never felt from anyone before. I could feel this ache spreading from my heart down into my pussy as I met him with my own unveiled love and desire. I think I could open this way because I felt that he couldn't have shut me out if he tried.

When our lips touched for the first time, we were transported to a place beyond our ego defenses. I know that sounds so psychological, but I don't know how else to describe it. I realized it was this defenselessness that I had been searching for all my life. When he would come over, we would sit close and lean our faces together. Everything was so slow like we were taking our time to open anew on each visit – to fully allow each other inside. His vulnerability was like a drug to me, because it allowed me into my own – I couldn't wait to take the next hit.

If mutual vulnerability is your central Core Desire, you may need to take the lead on vulnerability yourself. Often vulnerability invites vulnerability. You can also create a safe space for them to open to you in this way. You might say, "It doesn't matter that much to me what we do together, what matters is that you feel safe in our connection. I want to know if there is anything I can do to make you feel safe to share all of yourself with me. I also want to share all of myself with you. If you ever feel a barrier, I want you to let me know. I also want to hear all of your boundaries and share mine with you so we can trust each other to open in this vulnerable way."

Adept and Successful

Brandon was all about achievement when it came to sex. He told us about his hottest sexual experience and was always looking for new ways to turn his partners on.

Do you remember when James Cameron did his acceptance speech for Titanic and he said, 'I'm the King of The World'? That's what my best sexual experiences feel like. What gets me off the most is the feeling that I can make a woman so satisfied she will come back for more over and over. I've read every book and now I'm coming to you because I want to learn how to make women completely crazy in bed.

I think the hottest sexual experience I ever had was with a woman I met at the gym. She wasn't looking for anything serious, but we were friends with benefits for a while. This one time, she called me up and asked me to come over as soon as I could. Luckily, I had just jumped out of the shower so I was in an Uber in 10 minutes. I walked into her house and she couldn't keep her hands off me, so I took charge.

I felt like I could hear every single thing her body wanted from beginning to end. I knew just how to touch her, when and where. I warmed her up and teased her like crazy. When I reached down to finally start to touch her pussy, she was so wet her pussy juice was literally dripping onto her leg. I must have made her come at least 12 times that day. I made her come with my hand and she started squirting all over the place. Then, I made her come going down on her with my finger inside her. She was grabbing my head and squeezing it with her thighs and I was pretty sure the neighbors were going to call the police from all the noise. When I finally fucked her, she came almost immediately and then just kept coming. Yep, King of the World.

If your Core Desires are to be adept and successful, meaning you want to be very good at what you do and you gauge this by your partner's response, you might get lucky once in a while in the same way that Brandon did. It is much more rare than one might think for two people to have highly compatible movies, and Brandon just stumbled upon it with the woman at the gym. Additionally, the intensity and excitement of the experience might have been due to the fact that it was a new, no-strings-attached experience.

Over time, to keep sex hot, you need to really dial down and figure out a person's Core Desires and Hottest Sexual Movies. And the contents of this book are exactly how you can achieve this. Instead of thinking to yourself, "I need to know what the person wants without them having to tell me," it will be much more effective to hone your detective skills so you can find out what their Core Desires and Hottest Sexual Movies are. Giving someone their deepest desires is the surest way to take them to the heights of their pleasure.

If you want to feel adept and successful regularly in your sexual connections, you may need to initially let go of the idea that you should already know exactly how to please someone. While this may be part of the fantasy, it is not realistic to expect that you will be able to be a perfect lover to your partners without having to learn their particular desires.

In order to help someone open up to you about their turn-ons, getting the following points across will be the most helpful:

1. This is a safe space where you can share desires and will not be judged.
2. There is no right way or place to share your fantasies.
3. There is no pressure to tell me everything right away.
4. I want your feedback.
5. Anything can be a fantasy, and it doesn't have to be overtly sexual.

Your communication might go something like this:

"Nothing turns me on more than the feeling that I'm turning you on. The more I know about what gets you excited, the better. I want you to know that there is no pressure for you to tell me everything right away and I would never judge your desires. That being said, if you ever want to share anything that turns you on, don't wait for the right place or time to tell me one of your desires or fantasies. You can tell me in bed, in the car, over breakfast, in text, or in an email.

"There is also no wrong way to tell me. You can tell me directly, send me examples of scenes in movies, or shows that excite you or you can send me erotic stories that you'd like to play out. Also, I think that some people have a very narrow definition of what a fantasy is, but I think a fantasy is anything that makes you feel excited. For example, if you get really turned on by going together on a roller-coaster and holding hands at the scary parts, that counts as a fantasy as far as I'm concerned. So, it's not just about sex acts or positions or anything like that. I also would love any feedback that you have and there is also no wrong time to give me feedback."

Precious, Special, and Ravaged

Joaquin, a transgender man, shared his sexual fantasy about playing with lingerie.

I opened my box of treasures. As I pick out a creamy, beautiful, delicate lavender teddy, I feel my breath catch. Slipping into the lingerie, I become even more vulnerable than I am in my nudity.

I grew up in a harsh environment, where we were expected to abuse our bodies, to push through, to grit our teeth and do what needed to be done. I didn't believe that my body deserved anything soft or comforting, yet I desperately longed to be caressed, to be cared for, to be seen, and to be treated as special and precious.

I care for my lingerie the way I want to be cared for. I prepare my body for them, too, bathing myself lovingly and gently. As I dry myself and dress, I luxuriate in the sensation. I enjoy my time, alone, gazing at my own beauty and softness, all the contrast and the surprise and delight. I take time to bask in my gorgeousness.

I combine my cross-dressing with fantasy, imagining myself being dominated by fems. I fantasize about being recognized and chosen, seen as the special creature that I truly am, of having my secret exposed and admired. I imagine myself, too, being ravaged, my beautiful lingerie torn and then being tended to gently— my clothes as well as my body being mended and washed. I start masturbating through my clothes, and often I shift them so they are lightly binding me, so I am restrained both physically and mentally (by my desire to be gentle with them). I tend to myself and my clothes as aftercare, too, letting the fantasy spill into reality, loving myself the way I long to be loved.

If your Core Desires are to feel precious, special, and ravaged and your Hottest Sexual Movie is to dress in lingerie and be dominated, you might share the fantasy like this, "Lingerie makes me feel very erotic and I'd love to be able to incorporate it into our sexual experiences together. For me, the soft textures and lace of lingerie give me the feeling of being precious and I'd love to feel that from you.

"In addition to the lingerie I will wear for you, I'm also going to keep some lingerie lying around the room for you to use on my body in different ways. You might glide it gently across my body with your hands, or use one of my silky items to caress my skin. As I get more aroused, I'd like for you to move more into a place where you are taking me over and ravaging me. This means you could use the lingerie to bind my hands and feet or wrap it around me and use it to move my body into different positions. I'd also love for you to go back and forth between gently teasing and more aggressive, controlling touch."

These were just a few examples of Core Desires and Hottest Sexual Movies with tips on how to share them with a partner. As you might imagine, there are infinite variations and we hope these examples will inspire you to be very specific and detailed about what you really want.

Some Movies Are Easy to Share and Some Are Not

Some Hottest Sexual Movies are highly socially acceptable or socially acceptable enough that people feel comfortable embracing them, sharing them, and pursuing them out in the world. Other Hottest Sexual Movies are less socially acceptable and cause those who have them to feel more ashamed and isolated in their desires. Finally, there are some Hottest Sexual Movies that are much more challenging because they are self-destructive or illegal.

As we outline movies that are easy to share vs. those that are not, we will call attention to some of the likely feelings that people are trying to get by engaging in these Hottest Sexual Movies. As you read about different Hottest Sexual Movies and the feelings they inspire, try to relax judgment. Instead, engage with curiosity about your own Core Desires and Hottest Sexual Movies as well as those of your past or present partners.

Socially Acceptable Hottest Sexual Movies

In the United States, the most socially acceptable and celebrated Hottest Sexual Movies are romance and passion. These are the Hottest Sexual Movies that we literally see at the movies. Hollywood has provided us with endless examples of romantic imagery, depicting the timeless quality of endless love. Romantic Hottest Sexual Movies offer many Core Desires, including feeling *loved, adored, chosen, special, longed for, taken care of,* and *beautiful.*

Hollywood movies are also full of passionate immediacy, where the animal inside takes over as two people pull each other's clothes off to consummate their lust as quickly as possible. Passionate Hottest Sexual Movies offer people feelings such as being *desired, taken, irresistible,* and *sexy.*

Slightly less well-represented or socially acceptable, but very common Hottest Sexual Movies include dominance and submission as portrayed in such movies as The Secretary or 9 ½ weeks and made much more mainstream by the 50 Shades of Grey series. If you are dominant in your Hottest Sexual Movie, you may want to feel *powerful, in control, safe,* or *superior.* If you are submissive in your Hottest Sexual Movies, you may want to feel *humiliated, taken care of, used, punished,* or you may want *relief from responsibility.*

Also in this less-well-represented but socially acceptable category is what we call "the spiritual movie," which is well-depicted in the film Bliss. The spiritual movie is when people want to feel like their sexual union is sacred. Many sexuality teachers teach sacred sexuality practices such as tantra. Feelings that arise from the spiritual movie include *merged, connected, safe, held, or natural.*

These Hottest Sexual Movies are easier to share with a partner since there isn't much judgment or shame attached to them - they are well represented in mainstream media.

Less Socially Acceptable Hottest Sexual Movies

There are also a large number of Hottest Sexual Movies that bring up more shame in the people who have them because they do not fit in well with social norms and are not well-depicted in the media. When our clients come in with these Hottest Sexual Movies, they express hesitation in sharing them with a partner, and often feel isolated or demonized around their desires. We've included a few common examples below.

One example of a less socially acceptable feeling is *submissiveness* in a heterosexual man. Because submissive men are often not seen as masculine and there is a lot of pressure on heterosexual men to always portray a certain narrow definition of masculinity, many submissive men may have shame about their desire to be *dominated*. They may feel afraid to tell their partner, never giving them the chance to choose whether or not they would be willing to be dominant in bed.

It can also be a more difficult fantasy to fulfill. We see this in our office all the time. For whatever reason, be it nature or nurture (or, more likely, a combination of both), there are not nearly as many sexually dominant women out there as men who want to be dominated. For this reason, submissive men may have a hard time finding a dominant female partner. Many submissive men end up fulfilling their submissive fantasies through porn or by hiring a professional dominatrix (pro-domme) to fulfill these needs. Heterosexual men who want to feel *feminine* or *sexy* by wearing women's clothing face similar challenges around shame, judgment, and lack of compatible partners.

It seems like every week we learn about a new Hottest Sexual Movie that we'd never heard of before. One of our most recent favorites is Vore. Vore is the erotic desire to feel *consumed by* or *consume another* person or creature, including different types of fantasy creatures or monsters. Vore is different than other cannibalistic fantasies in that the person being consumed is generally consumed whole. In addition to feeling *consumed*, people who have vore fantasies may also want to feel *desired, overwhelmed, surrounded, or devoured.*

It is easy to see that the actual enactment of this fantasy is nearly impossible. Unless you want to try to get eaten whole by an orca or shark, you will probably not be able to fulfill this fantasy and, if you do, you won't ever be able to fulfill it again. Additionally, it is difficult to imagine that swiping on Tinder or meeting someone at a friend's party will match you up with another vore lover.

If you happen to have one of these more rare and hard-to-meet fantasies, the ideal scenario would be to find a partner who will fully embrace your fantasy and be willing to engage with you around it in some way (providing this is something you want). Perhaps they would be willing to watch animated Vore porn with you or whisper in your ear how they are going to swallow you whole as you are having sex. Who knows, you might even build yourself a sexy Vore monster you can get into together and have sex. Once you have an idea of what feelings you want to have, there can be so many fun ways to play with them.

Challenging Hottest Sexual Movies

Some people's life experiences cause them to have Core Desires and corresponding Hottest Sexual Movies that are challenging for some reason or another. At this point, we want to reiterate that you have no choice about the feelings you want to have and the kinds of fantasies that will most readily get you there cannot be changed. That being said, if you do have challenging Hottest Sexual Movies, there are ways that you can get at least some of your Core Desires met if you are willing to be creative with your Movie.

If Your Hottest Sexual Movies Are Self-Destructive

Some people's most efficient pathways to arousal also make their lives difficult to manage or put them in danger. Katie wanted to feel fully merged with her partners and also wanted to feel *complete* and total *trust in love*. One way that she played this out in her dating life was by not using condoms. She felt like condoms created a barrier between her and her partner and that requesting to use them made her partners feel like she didn't trust them, which took away her romantic fantasy of trusting in love. A part of her felt guilty and ashamed that she wasn't using condoms, but feeling guilty and ashamed did not lead her to change the behavior.

Another common example of a self-destructive pathway to arousal is dating people who are not good for you in some way, even though something about them is really arousing to you. For example, you may be aroused by *unavailability*, many people are. Many people had emotionally unavailable parents or were abandoned at a young age by one or both of their parents. The drive to get someone who is largely unavailable to pay attention to you or come towards you can be strong.

Getting someone who seems unattainable can be a huge turn-on because you feel *triumphant* where you felt like a failure in the past. You couldn't get the attention of a parent who left you or was there in body, but not in heart. Now you can get *attention* or *affection* at least for a short while, even if you feel alone and mistreated the rest of the time.

If you sometimes engage in behavior that is self-destructive, you may have a difficult time understanding why you continue to do it even though you know it is not good for you or others. Many people don't understand this, but we do not find it surprising at all.

First of all, the drive to get to our highest states of arousal is very strong. Secondly, guilt and shame are not generally good motivators for change. Instead of beating yourself up, try to bring curiosity and awareness to what you are doing. After all, there are some really amazing perks you are getting out of taking these risks or engaging in these relationships or behaviors.

Until you acknowledge the perks you are getting, you will not understand why you keep doing it. There is nothing wrong with wanting to experience the heights of your arousal. Once you have cultivated some acceptance for why you do what you do, then you may be ready to try getting these perks in ways that are less harmful to you.

1. Play out These Fantasies in Sex Instead of in Your Life

If you are unaware of the feeling you want to feel, you might find yourself playing out these desires in real life and getting challenging results. For example, you might be someone who is attracted to unavailable partners since you like to feel special by being able to get their attention. You've probably found yourself getting together with rejecting partners over and over again and end up heartbroken and feeling rejected.

If instead, you learn to play your fantasies out in the bedroom, you can find a loving partner, talk with them about what turns you on and ask them to play hard to get. They can learn how to start out cold and distant or a bit rejecting in the bedroom and then eventually come towards you. This way you can get your Core Desires without all of the negative side effects in your day-to-day life. To do this, you will need to find a partner who accepts your Core Desires and who is willing to help you play with them.

If you imagine you are the woman who was not asking her partner to wear condoms because she wanted to feel *merged* and *trusting*, you could have your partner whisper in your ear something directly about not using a condom even when they are using one. While you are having sex, your partner might say, "I'm sliding in and out of you raw, and nothing can ever come between us." Or, they could go for the Core Desires and separate it out from the condom. While using a condom, they could look in your eyes and say, "We are one, I know that you trust me completely and that's why you allow me inside of you, nothing can break our connection or our trust."

If you decide to shift the way you play sexually to lower self-harm you may find that it is just as arousing to do so. It is also possible that you will end up with lower levels of arousal, but a more safe, balanced, and stable day-to-day life. Only you can decide which choice to make and we never shame someone around these decisions.

2. Keep Doing What You Are Doing but Lower the Risk Any Way You Can

This approach is commonly known as harm reduction. Harm reduction was created to help folks who were addicted to drugs experience less harm from those addictions. Instead of assuming that everyone is capable of stopping using drugs, harm reduction assumes that some people won't be able to stop, but may be able to lower the risks associated with drug use.

If you were going to use a harm reduction model, and don't want to use condoms, you could get STD tested regularly and ask your partner(s) to do so. If you are someone who is having sex with partners who are at high risk of contracting HIV, you could use PReP. You could also use condoms sometimes - like at times you are at high risk for pregnancy or make sure you are using some other form of birth control. You could also use condoms with some partners, even if you don't use them with all of your partners.

In the case of choosing challenging partners, you might look for people who have the same psychological profile - avoidantly attached or narcissistic - but who have undergone some therapy. This way, at least they might be able to listen to your feelings sometimes and understand the impact on you of being in the relationship. For some, this can be soothing and balancing. Also, instead of trying to get all of your needs met from one unavailable person, you could consider dating multiple unavailable people. That way, if you really need someone at any particular time, you have more than one person to contact.

If Your Hottest Sexual Movie Is Illegal (But You Won't Actually Break the Law or Harm Anyone)

Before we talk about Hottest Sexual Movies that are actually illegal, we want to talk about people who have Hottest Sexual Movies that, if fully enacted, would be illegal, but who would not, in reality, harm someone. These are still challenging because a person may feel very ashamed to have them and may have trouble sharing them with a partner.

Mike's therapist called us asking what we could do to help him. He felt ashamed of his fantasies and desires and wanted more than anything to get rid of them. He was young and handsome and very sweet and gentle. His fantasies were all about hardcore rape, using women and fucking them again and again while they were gagged and tied up in his basement.

After speaking with Mike and his girlfriend, we discovered that he was very uncomfortable with his fantasies and that he was not at all violent. In fact, his girlfriend felt he was a bit overly gentle. We helped Mike see that his fantasies were quite common, and we traced back where they came from. When Mike was in junior high school, his female classmates constantly made fun of him. There was nothing he could do to get their approval so he started imagining taking them against their will. We helped him see that his fantasy was a desire to reclaim power after feeling humiliated.

We also gave him permission to have those fantasies and to allow himself to be aroused by them while separating them from taking any harmful action in the world. We pointed out that many women fantasize about those kinds of rape scenarios as well. And, even though he didn't want anything bad to happen to women, in reality, there were ways to play safely and consensually with this fantasy in the bedroom. He was very surprised and skeptical but also curious enough to keep coming and engaging in the coaching process.

We spent time in sessions helping him accept that the feelings he wanted to have in the bedroom - *being in control* and *dominant* - were normal and common. We also helped him look at the many different Hottest Sexual Movies that might bring him to those feelings. He was terrified that in order to be turned on and excited, he would have to get his full Hottest Sexual Movie. However, he found that simply talking about forcing someone or doing very mild power play was actually a huge turn-on for him.

At that point, he was ready to share his Core Desires and his Hottest Sexual Movie with his girlfriend. To his surprise, she was very turned on by his desires. Over time, they were able to negotiate what parts she was willing to actually play out with him and what parts he could verbally share with her during sex as a fantasy. Some of it they played out, other parts he told her, but did not actually enact. They both found the verbal fantasy sharing to be the most powerful and arousing part.

We wrote more about why women have rape fantasies in our book Making Love Real and felt it was good to share it here as well. Here is the excerpt (with a few pertinent updates) entitled "Understand Rape Fantasies":

About 80% of women fantasize about rape. Let us be clear here: women DO NOT want to be raped. Rape fantasies allow women to navigate the impossible dilemma of having desires but being seen as sluts if they act on them. A rape fantasy provides a work-around to this dilemma. It frees a woman from responsibility for willingly engaging in a sexual experience. In a rape fantasy, she has not made a conscious decision to have sex and therefore does not have to worry that she might be seen as a slut. In addition, rape fantasies allow a woman to safely explore Core Desires such as *being taken, used, forced,* or *submissive.* Also, she can play with the idea of experiencing men's animalistic desires without experiencing the actual terror and pain that come from real rape. Some women even like to play out these fantasies with their partners within boundaries in a safe environment.

You might ask yourself, why would a woman fantasize about something she doesn't actually want to happen? There are many reasons for this. In fantasies about rape, the woman might actually imagine herself in the role of the man, therefore experiencing the Core Desire of feeling *powerful* which she may have lost at an earlier time in her life when she felt powerless or violated. A woman might have a fantasy that is violating or painful that she doesn't want to actually enact; she simply wants to feel the full force of her arousal. Or a woman may have had a traumatic or less voluntary experience and now wants to reclaim her body and the experience in a safe environment with a trusted partner, gaining a sense of choice and power in a situation similar to the original experience, in which she had none.

If Your Hottest Sexual Movie Is Illegal (And You Are Willing to Break the Law)

You can see that Mike's fantasies are different than actually doing something that would break the law. Some people do have Hottest Sexual Movies that, when played out, would be breaking the law. For example, there are people who are turned on by non-consent or unilateral power, or who require the feeling of shocking someone in order to be aroused. Others like the feeling of corrupting innocence.

You might even be turned on by doing something because it's illegal - you might want to feel *naughty, daring, high*, or like the feeling of *breaking rules*. Some of the Hottest Sexual Movies that elicit these feelings are illegal. Some illegal Hottest Sexual Movies are more socially acceptable and even portrayed in movies such as taking drugs before sex or some version of public sex.

Examples of illegal and socially unacceptable behavior include drugging someone, incest, and peeping. We had one client who was arrested for indecent exposure.

Indecent Exposure

Our client Jim was a good example of someone who was trying to feel his Core Desires by engaging in an illegal Hottest Sexual Movie. In his childhood, Jim felt very disconnected from his parents. He didn't have friends growing up and he felt left out and invisible. At age 12, Jim was too sick to go to school so his mother kept him home. In the early afternoon, she went to the store leaving Jim home alone. As Jim lay on the couch, he began masturbating and, just as he was getting close to orgasm, a postal worker rang the doorbell.

The door was made of clear glass and when she peeked through the slatted blinds, she was startled. When her eyes met Jim's, he could see a high level of fear and distress in her eyes and then she ran away. This strong reaction was the opposite of feeling invisible. It was beyond simply being seen. By being frightening, he actually had a *big impact*. This feeling of being *scary, powerful* and *impactful* seared itself into his erotic composition and he came to us after having been arrested multiple times for indecent exposure.

His court-appointed therapist focused entirely on eradicating his flashing behaviors, which served only to exacerbate his shame. When he came to us, he was still engaging in risky flashing behaviors at beaches and in his car. We took a different approach. We helped him see that the feeling he wanted to have was a *strong emotional impact*. To gain the full force of his arousal, he scared and disgusted the other person.

First, we helped him see that there was nothing wrong with the feelings he wanted to have. These desires were part of who he was, were not of his making, and were very unlikely to change. We pointed out how hot and arousing it can be to have such an intense impact on someone else.

Once we had accepted and celebrated his desires, the next step was to help Jim meet those desires out in the world consensually, so that he would not harm others or be arrested and incarcerated again. We let him know that we didn't only care about the people he was exposing himself to, we cared about him and making sure that he was not harmed by future arrests. This helped him feel like he mattered.

We came up with a few places where he could be naked in front of other people legally, like nude beaches and sex parties. He found that if he could be naked in places where women would see him, he could fantasize that he had surprised them and that was almost as arousing as the real thing. At the sex parties, he was able to masturbate out in the open, and at the nude beaches, he would just get really turned on about being exposed and then go into a bathroom stall to masturbate.

Jim shared that the fact that we wanted to protect him and that we cared about him was a much different experience than he had had in the face of the criminal justice system or his therapist. He said that he had felt ashamed and continued engaging in non-consensual behaviors after working with therapists who were trying to cure him of his Core Desires, as opposed to finding consensual solutions.

To reiterate, while many therapies and health professionals are aimed at changing people's desires, we do not believe these desires are changeable. Our approach is to embrace and celebrate the desires, and help lower people's shame, while at the same time making sure they meet those desires out in the world with other consenting adults. This helps them avoid harming others and also helps them stay out of harm's way themselves.

How to Teach Your Partner Your Hottest Sexual Movie

Now it's time to teach your partner your Hottest Sexual Movie! You may have many Hottest Sexual Movies, however, it will be helpful to teach your partner one movie at a time. Before you start, there are a few topics we need to cover, namely boundaries, having a safeword, trying new things, the benefit of the doubt, asking for what you want, and having realistic expectations.

You Have a Right to Your Boundaries

*Please Remember: It is **not** your job to do anything you **don't** want to do!*

You and your partner both have a right to boundaries. In fact, it is essential that you keep your boundaries as best you can in your relationship and your sex life to create trust and avoid building resentment. It is also important to remember that your boundaries may shift. A "no" right now doesn't shut the door forever. When you both feel permission to keep your boundaries, you will be able to relax and feel safer exploring. Each of you will also change and grow.

When it comes to boundaries, what was a strong "no" at one point might become a "maybe" or a "yes" later. A "yes" might also turn into a "no." This does not mean you should push your partner to widen their boundaries; quite the contrary. What you want to do is give your partner the feeling that you embrace their boundaries and support them in taking good care of themselves by not letting their boundaries be crossed. The more a person feels like you are on their side, the more safe they feel to open.

If your sexual boundaries have been crossed in the past non-consensually (for example, if you have experienced sexual abuse or rape), or if you have let them be crossed in the past or in your current relationship, you may need to keep your boundaries quite strong at first before you can let yourself trust again. Often when couples face boundary challenges, the person who needs strong boundaries feels guilty and the other feels rejected. As a result, the boundaries continue to get pushed and crossed over and over again. If this is your dynamic, you may need some support in learning how to negotiate boundaries so that you will be able to reconnect emotionally and sexually. Long-term boundary challenges can result in resentment, shutdown, and sexual dysfunction.

When your partner shares their desires with you, you might feel pressure to give them what they want. It is important to understand the difference between accepting each other's desires and having to fulfill them. It is scary to let some of your partner's desires remain unfulfilled. Yet if you try to do things for your partner that are not in alignment with who you are, you will probably feel bad about yourself and/or begin to shut down and resent your partner. Also, many people will be able to feel you are not really enjoying it and then they won't get what they want from it anyway if you are just going through the motions, but hate doing what you are doing.

Instead of giving your partner things you don't want to give, we suggest that you take two steps. The first is to hear and accept your partner's desire. Listen with generosity and excitement, knowing you can separate between listening enthusiastically and participating. The second is to see if the desire or some part of it is something that you feel comfortable fulfilling. For many people, having their desires heard and accepted is what makes them feel loved and connected. Others will want their desires to be met, but you might not be able to do that for them.

Every relationship has disappointment in it. Our aim with Coming Together is to help you maximize what is possible in terms of you and your partner fulfilling one another's desires without crossing boundaries. Later on in the book, we will talk more about what to do when you have done everything you can to maximize your erotic potential together and there are still needs that are unmet.

Have a Safeword

Before you start with any of the Hottest Sexual Movie exercises, it can be helpful to have a safeword. A safeword is a word other than "stop" that you can use when something is happening that you don't want to happen. A safeword is wonderful because it gives you the feeling that you can try new things knowing that you and your partner have agreed that you will stop whenever you hear each other's safewords.

Safewords are a great tool for many reasons. The first is that it can sometimes be difficult to say "stop" because it feels harsh or rejecting. A safeword conveys that you don't like something in a somewhat softer or more playful way. Secondly, sometimes people like to play with fantasies around non-consent. In these sexual situations, you may want to be able to say "stop" or "don't" or "get off of me," but actually want your partner to keep going. If you have a safeword, then you can say all of those other things, but your partner will only stop if you say that particular word.

When choosing a safeword, it is helpful to choose a word that you don't normally say during sex. The most common, generic safeword is "red," like a traffic light signaling you to stop. Some people use both "red" and "yellow", where red means stop and yellow means don't stop, just back off a little bit. For example, if your partner is flogging you and you want them to keep going, but to just do it a bit more gently. You can also make up your own personal safeword that can be a fun, inside joke for you. For example, it might be something you hate like "rollercoaster" or "anchovy".

Try on a Try-Something-New Attitude

No matter how long you have been together, if you have not approached your sex life consciously, with curiosity and open communication, there will be a learning curve. You can log many years of unsatisfying sex together without any improvement if you don't experiment. Trying something new can be scary, as it may bring up fears and inadequacies as well as memories of negative experiences together. But trying new things, exploring new ways of communicating around sex, and discussing needs and desires are essential to creating a good sex life.

Trying something new requires bravery and gentleness with yourself and your partner. Often when we invite couples to try something new, they feel awkward or goofy at first. When you first try a new experience, you might feel like laughing or making jokes. You might feel so uncomfortable that you want to give up. All of these feelings are normal.

Again, see if you can be gentle with yourself and each other as you begin to share more openly and take the risks of trying something new.

Trying it once doesn't mean you have to do it forever. In order to feel free while experimenting, it is essential to know that you always have a choice. You can try things out and see what is arousing and interesting for you and what isn't. Not every sexual activity or attitude is right for every person, and you will need to accept your own and your partner's right to try something then decide if they like it or not.

Also, if you ask your partner for something and then realize that it doesn't feel as good as you imagined it, or only feels good when you're more aroused, feel free to say so. You can always change your mind. What works in your fantasy might not work in reality, and what works one time might not work for you forever.

Give Each Other the Benefit of the Doubt

Trust that each of you wants to please the other. If there is something you want from your partner and you have asked for it, but they have not given it to you, there are some likely explanations, the least of which is that they are purposely trying to deny you pleasure. More likely, they are trying very hard to give you what you want, but they may feel insecure or confused. They may not know exactly how to give it to you, they may be afraid to try for fear of doing it wrong, or they may be trying to learn under stressful circumstances.

If you are asking for what you need from a place of frustration or criticism, your partner may be triggered. When people are triggered emotionally, their ability to learn shuts off. For this reason, you must be patient and forgiving with your partner as they learn. While you might have a precise picture in your mind of how you want to be touched, seduced, and talked to, it can be challenging for your partner to know exactly what you mean. Feedback and repetition are essential to the learning process.

For example, when we teach men how to seduce women, we do an exercise called "Up Against the Wall." In this exercise, we throw them up against the wall with passion and desire and then they take a turn throwing us. Whenever we teach this to men, we tell them that they won't do it perfectly on the first try. We always assume that they are doing their best and that, if they are not getting it right away, it's because they just need more gentle demonstrations, information, and feedback. They also need to practice, practice, practice.

On average, men will throw us against the wall about ten times in a session. Each time, we tell them everything they did that worked well for us and give them a couple of pieces of feedback about what could be better. We might say, "I loved it when you leaned in and smelled my neck; that was so perfect. When you come back out, make sure you come back into full eye contact before moving on to something else." Or "Your big hands feel so good on my hips, and I'd love it if the grip around my waist were stronger."

We don't want to give you false hope. Many people are able to learn new skills and become much more adept at pleasing one another. At the same time, there will be some things that are impossible for you or your partner to learn. Again, once you've tried many times using a gentle, inviting, and non-judgmental approach, it is possible that the learning won't happen. Again, we will talk about what to do in this situation a little bit later.

The bottom line is that when you give your partner the benefit of the doubt, you will be more likely to approach them with a positive attitude and they will be more likely to learn what you need.

Ask for Anything and Everything You Want

In order to get to really get your Hottest Sexual Movie, you will need space in your relationship to ask for what you want. There are no right or wrong requests. When your partner asks what turns you on, you might think that the only appropriate answer is some sort of overtly sexual act or touch technique, but that is just one of the many requests you can make.

What turns most people on has much more to do with psychological arousal than physiological, so just asking for how you want to be touched is not enough. For example, you might feel like it's okay to ask your partner for a lighter touch, but not okay to ask them to tell you what an amazing ass you have.

It is helpful to let your partner know what kinds of experiences get you in the mood to have sex in the first place, whether it be a walk in nature together, a sensual massage, a solo bath, a sexy dance party in the living room, dressing up and going out somewhere, getting sexts from your partner, or being grabbed and passionately kissed in the middle of the day.

Also, your partner may be thinking all sorts of wonderful, loving, and desirous thoughts about you but not know which ones will land well or how best to say them. If you help out by telling them, then they have a chance to do it right. The more specific you are, the more likely you are to get what you want. Try not to get frustrated when they don't get it right away or they don't remember all the time. You will likely need to ask for the things that you want more than once to help your partner make giving them to you a habit.

Have Realistic Expectations

So often, when people come to our office, they are trying to "get the spark back." The translation of this is that they want their sex life to look and feel like it did at the beginning of their relationship. While we would love to wave a magic wand and bring back all of the desire that novelty and uncertainty inspires, this is not a realistic hope. What you can actually get out of learning each other's Hottest Sexual Movies is a much deeper intimate connection and pathway to much hotter sex. Instead of looking backward and hoping you can have what was, see if you can look towards creating something entirely different and looking towards what's possible.

It is also helpful to be realistic about the learning curve. It will take time to teach each other what you really want sexually. Some parts might be easier for your partner to learn than others. Remember, learning the new skills involved in giving your partner hot sex is an embodied learning process. If you think about the other embodied learning processes you have gone through, like learning a musical instrument, a sport, how to partner dance, etc., you already know that this kind of learning takes practice, repetition, and ongoing feedback.

If you ask your partner for something once or only try to teach them once, it is very likely that they will not be able to give it to you. Like any other embodied learning process, you (or a coach) will have to help them learn all of the different aspects of your movie. You will have to help them understand the setting, tone, touch, words, etc. and give them a chance to practice, make mistakes, and get feedback. If you are learning your partner's movie, you will need to be gentle on yourself, be willing to make mistakes, and be open to receiving feedback.

Finally, you may have discovered Coming Together near the beginning of your relationship when you are still feeling a lot of empathy and connection with your partner, or you may have been suffering in an unsatisfying sexual relationship for many years. It is definitely more difficult to come back from a ton of resentment than it is to create something sustainable closer to the beginning of a relationship.

If you have built up a lot of resentment, you may need a place to do some venting to someone other than your partner. You may also need to do some work to reconnect with your feelings of empathy towards one another. It is very difficult to dive right into trying to make sex hot again if the empathy isn't there. You will probably need to share and hear each other's resentments without defending yourselves. In these talks, the most important thing is to really get how your partner has felt let down, left out, criticized, hurt, or abandoned by you. If you need help clearing resentments, check out our other book *Making Love Real: The Intelligent Couples Guide to Lasting Intimacy and Passion.*

The Building Blocks of a Movie

In order to share your movie, you need to be able to describe in detail what you want. There are five different aspects that you can think of as the building blocks of a movie: the story (which we talked about earlier in the section "How to talk about Your Hottest Sexual Movie"), the energy, the touch, the words, and the gestures. By doing the mini-exercises in this section, you will start to build your Hottest Sexual Movie repertoire.

Feel the Energy

The energy of a sexual experience refers to the level of intensity that the experience has. It can range from low to high and from out of control to highly controlled. Romance generally has a lower and somewhat controlled intensity, while dominance is generally a higher but still controlled intensity. Passion has high intensity and feels out of control.

Energy is modulated by the breath, so make sure that whenever you are touching each other's bodies and sharing erotic energy, you are breathing. Controlled energy is achieved through slow, deep breath, while out of control energy usually causes the breath to quicken. Eye contact is also a way to transmit energy, as is your facial expression. Eye contact can be very soft or much more intense; you may be smiling or being very serious.

Exercise:
Practice With the Energy

Tell and teach your partner what kind of energy you want to have from them. Do you like it when the energy goes up and down during a sexual experience or do you want it to just keep building and building? No matter what, don't forget to breathe!

Let your partner know if you want them to be controlled in their energy and leading, or more out of control and experiencing the moment without consciously leading. Share with your partner if you want a slow pace where the energy builds or for the energy to be fast and intense right away.

Let them know if you want their energy to feel more like it is open and spacious or directed and penetrating. Tell your partner what kind of eye contact you like, if any. Do you want gentle eyes or intense eyes? Smile or no smile? Or do you want to move between these?

Explore Touch

Different qualities and types of touch offer different kinds of feelings. For example, a light touch on the cheek can make you feel *precious, loved, adored, seen, delicate, cared for* while holding down someone's wrists during sex can make you feel *powerful* or *in control*. Being held down can make you feel *helpless* and being grabbed passionately can make you feel *wanted* or *overwhelmed*. Regardless of what you or your partner want to feel, make sure when you touch, you are touching for your own pleasure as well as your partner's. If you are only doing it for them, they will not feel your desire.

 ## Exercise:
The Touch That Touches You

Show your partner how you like to be touched and tell them what the touch makes you feel. Do you like light, feathery caresses? Do you like forceful grabs? What parts of your body do you most like to have touched? When your partner touches these parts, what does it make you feel? You might say something like, "I love it when you cup my ass gently when we are doing something that is not sexual. This makes me feel desired, reassured, and held by you." Then, show them the way you like your ass cupped. When your partner shows you, give it a try and practice with feedback until you feel like it's right.

Or, "I like it when you hold around my neck when we are in missionary position and you are inside of me. It makes me feel like I am *at your mercy* and there is no escape." And again, show them the way you like your neck held and make sure you do practice with feedback.

Remember, this might be awkward at first. Let yourself be light and playful then start to take it more seriously when you get the hang of it.

Express With Words

Many couples have silent sex, where the focus is mostly on sexual acts. However, words can help deepen the engagement in a sexual experience. This is especially true for women, who are usually more distractible during sex. Also, some women get tired of words being mostly about their body parts although other women really love this. You can always ask! A good way to translate your appreciation of their physical appearance is to say how it makes you feel. Instead of saying "You have a nice ass," you can say, "When I grab your ass, I feel *turned on, hungry* or *powerful.*"

For some people, words can be very distracting. Let your partner know if you like talking during sex and whether you like to talk, be talked to, or both. If words are difficult for you because you feel like you are acting or they seem cheesy, see if you can just say what you sincerely feel towards the person.

 Exercise:
Talk Sex

Words can include direct statements about the other person, how you feel about them, what you want to do to them, what you want them to do, fantasies, etc.

Sit with your partner and think of a sentence that you want your partner to say to you that touches your Core Desire in some way. Tell them the sentence and what it makes you feel. An example would be, "I want you to tell me that no one else makes you feel like I do. When you say this, I feel *special.*" or "Please tell me I'm a naughty little slut and that I'm going to get what I deserve. When you say this, I feel *dirty* and like I'm going to get *punished.*" You might say, "I want you to call me your Goddess, and to tell me that you want to worship at the altar of my yoni. This makes me feel *connected to you* and *spiritual.*"

Make sure you demonstrate how you want them to say it. For example, do you want it whispered in your ear or said with passion looking directly in your eyes? Don't worry about getting too creative or in-depth. You may simply want your partner to whisper your own name in your ear with desire in their voice. Hearing your own name might give you the feeling of being *uniquely desired.*

Show With Gestures

For some movies, there are also gestures that you can make both during and outside of sex that can keep the feeling of the movie going, such as giving someone a heart-shaped chocolate or buying them a collar that sybolizes your dominant/submissive relationship.

 Exercise:
Give a Gesture

Tell your partner a gesture that would turn you on and touch your Core Desire.

Find Your Teaching and Learning Style

There are many ways to teach and learn each other's movies and you will want to find the right way for you. Be aware that the best way for you may not be the best way for your partner, so you will need to share your needs and be open to your partner's learning needs as well. If you are doing this as a couple without outside help, you can teach each other with a workshopping approach or during sexual experiences. If you are having trouble teaching and learning from each other, you might also consider hiring a coach.

Workshop It

For some people, it is much easier to teach and/or learn by thinking of the experience as more of a workshop than trying to create a whole successful sexual experience. A workshop approach will also make it safe to try things without having to do them perfectly. Being in workshop mode means doing the following:

Experiment Without Goals

People often feel that sex with a partner must follow a specific trajectory, where arousal is supposed to build and build and both people eventually reach orgasm. In sex, you might expect things to go relatively smoothly and for both people to come out of the experience sexually satisfied. If your movies are different enough, this has likely not been the case for you. If you have realized that there are some things that need to change about your sex life in order for it to be mutually fulfilling, it can be really wonderful to lower the pressure. It is quite unlikely that either or both of you will end up satisfied as you are going through the learning process.

For this reason, it is helpful to look at workshopping as experimenting without having a specific outcome in mind. This will allow you to relax and see how you feel about each different activity you are engaging in.

Activate Learning Mode

In general, sex is more of an experience than a learning process. During a sexual encounter, you are more likely to be trying to go with the flow than actually bringing awareness to what you are doing. Thinking of it as a workshop will encourage your learning brain to awaken, and you will approach it like other learning experiences where the goal is trying to pick up new skills. Use trial and error. When you are teaching each other how to give one another your Hottest Sexual Movies, try something, get feedback, and try again. This is the fastest way to pick up new skills.

Use Curiosity and Playfulness

When you are workshopping your Hottest Sexual Movies, bring an attitude of curiosity. Your partner will be much more likely to open up all of their deepest desires to you if they feel you genuinely want to know what turns them on. It is very vulnerable to share these desires, and people are likely to give up quickly on teaching if you do not seem fully interested and engaged in the experience.

Also, it is important that you don't take things too seriously, while at the same time not making a joke out of your own or your partner's desires. The best thing you can do is approach this exploration with fun and playfulness. If you are terse and frustrated with your partner, you probably won't get very far. Most people are incapable of learning if they are triggered, and having a partner frustrated with you can be very triggering. On the other hand, if you are able to laugh together about the times when things don't work perfectly, the whole experience of learning can actually be very bonding, and learning will go much quicker.

Teach Your Partner Experientially

It's one thing to tell your partner, "I need you to be more sensual," or "Your kissing is too rough," or "I want your tone to be domineering" and another thing entirely to demonstrate what you mean. When you are workshopping your movie, it will be much more effective to show them than tell them. After all, sensual can mean something very different from one person to the next and it's hard to imagine what you might mean by domineering unless you do it to them first.

Give Gentle and Specific Feedback

Feedback is essential to the learning process. This is because what you want is completely different than what someone else wants. So, you need to gently and supportively help your partner learn about your desires. You can give feedback on the lightness or firmness of touch, the energy your partner is bringing, the words that they are using, or the tone they are using when they speak.

Whenever you demonstrate something and your partner gives it a try, let them know what you liked about what they did first and then tell them as specifically as possible what you'd like to be different. For example, you can say, "I love the way you touched me so lightly up and down my arm. After you've done it once, it would feel better to me if you'd move to a different part of my body so it doesn't feel repetitive." After telling them, then show them what you mean. Another example might be, "The way you looked at me just then made my pussy tingle! When you are bossing me around, can you be a little more stern? Here, let me give you an example of the way I like it said to me."

If what they offer you feels great, make sure you let them know how great it was and how much you appreciate their willingness to take the time to learn about your desires.

 Exercise:
Have a Workshop Date (Or Many!)

1) Schedule a date night with your partner to do some ongoing Hottest Sexual Movie workshops together. When you are learning, it is best to focus on one person's movie at a time as much as possible. If you find you keep putting this learning off, you will need to look under the surface to see what is making you avoid it and talk with your partner about it, or talk with a coach.

2) Keep your boundaries. We know we've said it a thousand times, but remember, if there is anything your partner asks you to do that you don't want to do, see if there is something similar that you might be interested in. For example, you might say, "I'm not really

comfortable slapping you in the face, but I'm willing to spank you on your ass or other places." If there is nothing else you want to do in that realm, you will simply need to say, "I'm not comfortable with that."

3) Share your feeling words. You might say something like, "During sex, I want to feel like we are escaping into another world together. I want us to feel *adventurous, free,* and *open* with each other during the experience.

4) Listen to your partner's feeling words and tell them how you feel about what they shared. For example, you might say, "I'm really excited to learn your movie. I also feel a little insecure that I might not be able to give you what you need because I can be a little inhibited, but I'm willing to give it a try. I hope you won't take it personally if I giggle sometimes, that's just me getting past my embarrassment. It's never that I think your desires are silly."

5) Share some experiences from one of your Hottest Sexual Movies that you want to practice during this workshop. Here are a few examples of requests that someone who wants to feel *adventuresome* and *free* might make. To prepare, you might make a similar list. Then, when you come together, share and practice them one at a time. Make sure you give and receive feedback after each new experience:

   a) You can say: "One thing that makes me feel very free is when we get naked and do normal things around the house together. Can we get naked now and go downstairs and make a light champagne cocktail to bring to the rest of our workshop?"

b) And: "The next thing that makes me feel very free is if we stay naked and start to do playful, fun things together. For example, I'd love for us to have a pillow fight or wrestle but without anyone trying too hard to win."

c) And: "There are some words that make me feel really free. You could say, 'I love playing with you' or 'It feels so good to be on this wild ride together', or 'I want us to screw in every room in the house tonight.' Even if we don't have sex in every room, it's so fun to hear you say it."

d) And: "I would love it if you would pick me up and twirl me around."

6) Make sure you have some loving closure around your workshop time. You might end with a 10 minute cuddle or with each of you giving the other person a verbal appreciation (or both).

Teach During Sex

For some people, it feels inauthentic to workshop sex and they can't get into the experience. They feel awkward and like they are being observed. Also, there can be less arousal in a workshopping approach and, for some people, arousal is what disinhibits them enough to be more overtly sexual.

For these folks, it will be much easier to learn during a sexual experience as opposed to a workshopping experience. If you do decide to teach during sex, it is still important to have realistic expectations. The learning will need to take place slowly during the course of many sexual experiences.

To teach your partner what you want and learn what they want during sex, you will need to:

Be Directive in a Sexy and Seductive Way

Invite your partner to give you what you want by seducing them into it. To do this, you will need to stay in your erotic mode when asking and giving feedback. One of the biggest mistakes we see people make in these situations is what we call "jumping out." Jumping out is when you are in the middle of a sexual experience and you want your partner to do something different and you completely change out of your erotic mode. You move into a teacher mode where you are lecturing them on what to do or, even worse, telling them all the things that they are doing wrong.

Instead, stay in the moment of your arousal, and guide them gently with a sexy voice to do what you want them to do. "Mmmmm, that feels so good when you suck my nipples, I'd love it if you'd bite them as well...Oh, yes, even a little harder would be better for me." Another example is, "God, I love the way you suck my cock. When you are sucking me, can you take breaks and look up at me and tell me how good my cock feels in your mouth and how you couldn't wait to suck it?"

Demonstrate What You Want Done to You

Another way to get what you want sexually is to ask if you can show them something you really like and then ask them to do it back to you. You might say, "Can I whisper a fantasy in your ear and then you whisper one back in mine? I love hearing sexy stories when I'm being fucked." Or, "I really like dirty talk, I'm going to talk dirty to you and then I would love to hear you do it back to me."

Ask What They Want and Give Them a Menu

If you want to find out more about what your partner wants, you can always take the direct route and simply ask, "Is there anything you want me to do or say to you?" Unfortunately, many people don't have a good answer to this question. If the answer is, "Everything you are doing is great," but you still want to fine-tune, you can give them multiple options and then ask which they like better or if they like both. For example, you can say, "Do you prefer it when I call you a good girl or a bad girl or both, or neither." If they don't know, you can say, "Let me try it out and you tell me which turns you on more." Or, you can gently suck their nipple, then bite a little harder and ask if they like one better than the other or both.

Get Coaching

While it might be difficult to imagine having a stranger help you have better sex with your partner, sometimes, it is exactly what you need. If you are an individual, it can be very helpful to get real, honest, and gentle feedback from a professional who understands how arousal works. If you are a couple, you may have tried to teach each other your desires and it isn't hasn't gone well or you might simply have no idea how to begin. It can also be helpful to hear something from a neutral person that your partner may have been telling you for a long time. It can be easier to hear it from someone you are not in a relationship with because it will bring up less defensiveness in you.

If You Are in a Relationship

Somatica Sex and Relationship Coaches are specifically trained to help you figure out your Core Desires. They can also help you share, construct, and teach each other your Hottest Sexual Movies.

When utilizing a coach to help you unearth, communicate, and learn each other's movies, you may want to do it as a couple or you may want to do some individual work first and then come back together and practice. It depends a lot on where you are in your process with one another and there are good arguments for both.

Reasons you might want to learn together:

- A fun, bonding process - if you are in a good place with one another and there is not too much resentment or frustration already built up, you may find that learning together can be a lot of fun and can help you build intimacy and connection. Many couples enjoy learning, laughing (and, of course, sometimes crying) together through the process.

- Giving personalized and specific teaching and feedback - if you decide to have a coach teach your partner, they can speak with you and practice with you a bit to get a good idea of what you want. However, what your partner will learn and the feedback they will get will be a little more generic and less specific to your perfect movie. If you decide to be part of the process, you will be able to be much more specific about your desires and feedback throughout the process. Of course, if they do learn a bit on their own, they can always come back and fine-tune with you.

Reasons why you might want to let your partner learn some skills on their own before trying them out on you:

- Low-pressure learning - one of the great things about learning on your own as opposed to learning with a partner, is that it can feel easier to make mistakes and try again. Because you are not in an intimate relationship with your coach, you will likely worry less about disappointing them and will also feel less defensive when they give you feedback because you won't be emotionally enmeshed with them.

- Partner frustration and resentment - if you have been trying to teach your partner for a while or have been building resentment, it might be better to send your partner to do some learning on their own. It is very difficult for someone to learn when they are triggered. If you are teaching with a frustrated attitude or are critical, your partner will likely shut down and have a hard time learning, which will just exacerbate the problem. Giving them some space to learn from someone who is not frustrated will likely accelerate the learning curve.

- Keeping the mystery - if you are someone who likes the feeling of being *swept off their feet* and not knowing what your partner is going to do next, it might be helpful to let them do some learning on their own. Even if you have to explain what you want to a coach and they teach it to your partner, it will still retain more of the mystery than if you have to teach them step-by-step yourself.

Working together as a couple or working separately, both have their place and their specific benefits. It is really helpful for you to know who you are and be honest with your partner about which will be most helpful. It is also possible, and often best, to do a hybrid of the two - spend some time learning apart and then some time bringing it all together as a couple.

If You Don't Have a Partner

If you are single but want to learn how to seduce a partner or really relax into and enjoy sex, you can learn and practice all of this on your own with a Somatica® coach. In individual sessions, the coach connects with you erotically and emotionally within boundaries, so that you can practice in real-time and receive clear, honest feedback.

If you want to learn how to be a better lover, your coach will teach you a wide variety of Hottest Sexual Movies that will likely please a very broad spectrum of people you want to date. You will also learn how to offer a wide variety of erotic experiences while attuning to and reading your partner's non-verbal cues. This way, you know which ones excite them and continue to fine-tune your approach to access their Core Desires.

If you want to learn how to relax into the pleasures of sex, your coach will offer different kinds of erotic experiences and you can learn how to immerse yourself in them. Your coach will also help you discover what you want and help you practice giving your partner direction and feedback in a sexy way.

Teaching Your Movie is an Ongoing Process

Teaching your partner your movie will be an ongoing process throughout your relationship. It takes time for people to learn each other's desires and our desires change over time. So, don't expect your partner to get it right the first time (or the fifth time) you tell them or show them what you want. Be patient and continue to give lots of positive feedback about anything they are doing right and then continue to gently redirect them around things that are not working for you.

Looking at teaching as an ongoing process will also leave room for changes, creativity, growth, and mutual exploration and expansion. While our Core Desires don't change, many times your Hottest Sexual Movies need new flavors to keep them exciting.

Part III

Enhance Your Sexual Compatibility

Sexual Compatibility

Sexual compatibility is when two people are able to feel fulfilled by having sex with each other. In order for sex to be hot, it must fulfill a good deal of your own and your partner's Core Desires through one or more Hottest Sexual Movies. Unfortunately, our culture promotes the belief that people who are "meant for each other" will automatically have amazing sex without ever having to identify or communicate what they want. This belief is exacerbated by the fact that most relationships have a "honeymoon period."

The honeymoon period is generally the first six to eighteen months of a relationship. During this period, you may be able to have super hot sex with your partner even if you are not particularly sexually compatible. You might even have hot sex without having to tell your partner anything about what you want. When you are with someone new, it is possible to project all of your fantasies on to them, and these projections can be enough to fuel the fires of desire and arousal that lead to a lot of sexual fulfillment. What's more, the uncertainty of new romance can be very arousing because you have no idea if they will keep choosing you or not.

Once in a while, two people get together who happen to have complementary turn-ons and so the Hottest Sexual Movies they play out with each other are highly compatible. It is likely that couples who experience this will stay satisfied even after the honeymoon period is over. Unfortunately, most people don't end up with high enough compatibility that they are able to get their Hottest Sexual Movies met ongoing in spontaneous sexual encounters without any communication.

The sexual honeymoon period doesn't happen for everyone. For those who do get to experience it, a majority will see it fading as the excitement of newness and uncertainty wears off and the differences in their Hottest Sexual Movies start to cause a sexual disconnect. This is when people begin to search for answers to why this is happening and often look in all the wrong places. They may attribute it to hormonal changes or fear that their partner is losing interest in them. They may think they just need to buy a new toy or try something new, but they don't know what they actually need to try.

It is then that the important question arises: "How can you keep sex hot in long-term relationships?" It seems like everywhere we look, we see new one-size-fits-all approaches to answering this question. Therapists, coaches, sexperts, popular magazines, and new age teachers have offered a variety of potential solutions.

Some sexuality teachers will say that there needs to be polarity between the masculine and feminine. While this will help some couples whose desires include the need for polarity, others will be turned on by a feminine-feminine or masculine-masculine dynamic.

Leading sexperts might tell you that there needs to be more mystery and distance that counters the domesticity. Yes, for some, that might be just the thing that would turn them on. For others, however, less mystery and more safety will be what allows them to open to another.

Some couples' therapists advocate the idea that deep attunement and good communication will automatically lead to good sex, but that's only true if your Core Desires have something to do with *attuning* or *being attuned to*. It is just as possible that what gets you off is that someone wants to use you for their pleasure and who purposefully ignores your needs in the process.

The reason these approaches will not necessarily fix your sex life is that they try to impose one type of Hottest Sexual Movie onto the extremely diverse landscape of human desire. And, they don't take into account each person's Core Desires.

The good news is that it is possible to become more sexually compatible! If you are part of a couple who has less complementary sexual desires, you will need to learn about your partner's Hottest Sexual Movie and teach them yours so that you can create experiences together that fulfill both of your desires. If you are less inherently compatible, you will need to find ways to bridge your Hottest Sexual Movies or take turns playing out one another's.

Sexual Challenges That May Stem From Not Getting Your Hottest Sexual Movie

Many sexual dysfunctions stem from not getting your Core Desire and Hottest Sexual Movies met. The most common for men include psychological erectile dysfunction (ED) and decreased libido. Many men also worry about being dependent on porn for their sexual satisfaction. For women, the most common sexual dysfunctions include low desire or challenges with arousal and orgasm.

Unfortunately, if a person goes to the doctor or a couples' therapist, these experts have very little training in how arousal works so they offer hormones, medication or better emotional communication. While there may occasionally be hormonal, medical or emotional causes, it's much more likely that the problem is around not getting your Hottest Sexual Movie. You may be able to avoid medical interventions, long-term disappointment and unhappiness, self-doubt, and feelings of being broken by addressing the cause instead of treating the symptoms.

Psychological Erectile Dysfunction (ED)

Finding your Core Desire and experiencing your Hottest Sexual Movie is one very common answer to the problem of psychological erectile dysfunction in men. One way to tell if your ED is psychological as opposed to physiological (medical) is if your ED is situational as opposed to across-the-board. In other words, if you have morning wood and have no problem getting an erection when you masturbate, but can't get one with partner sex, then you likely have Psychological ED. If you do have across-the-board ED, make sure you see your doctor as it can be an early sign of heart disease.

So often, when men come into our office with ED, they feel that they are supposed to be aroused and get hard as a result of any sexual interaction available to them. While this might be true for a 19-year-old (though not always, and we have definitely worked with young men who have psychological ED), as you get older and your hormones decrease, what really turns you on becomes more and more essential to your arousal.

Unless you want to bypass the whole issue and pop a pill (which many times doesn't even work), it is essential that the sex you are having is arousing for you. A much more sustainable way is to figure out and communicate your Core Desires and guide your partner towards your Hottest Sexual Movie.

Alex came to us complaining that he could not stay hard during sex with new women he would date. He would get really excited at the thought of having sex with them, however, when the time came, he was unable to get an erection. His biggest complaints were that the women he was dating were very passive. He had to make the first move, the second move, and on and on. It turned out the feeling he wanted to have was being *seduced*.

Unfortunately, this is a more difficult feeling if you are a heterosexual man than a woman since women are socialized to wait for their partners to make all of the moves so that they won't be seen as sluts. Also, many women have the fantasy of being *desired* or *taken* and don't expect to have to be the one to seduce.

We came up with a good approach for Alex to use that would help him turn the tables on his dates. He would make the first move in terms of kissing and then escalate with some touch. He would take her shirt off and his, but keep the seduction nice and slow. He would then wait until a woman eventually put her hand on his dick. Once she did, he would say, "Oh, I'm not actually ready to have sex yet," which was true. He was not ready to have sex, and would not be until they took over the escalation process.

When he tried it out in the world it worked like a charm. Suddenly, the woman was put in the role of moving the action along and she had to switch from the role of seduced to seducer. Once she was going after him with desire, he was able to get aroused and erect and his dating life began to get way more fun and interesting.

Low Desire

Both women and men suffer from low sexual desire, or decreased libido, though it is much more common in women. In fact, it is the most common female sexual dysfunction and women come into our offices all the time complaining of low desire or difficulty becoming aroused or orgasming with a partner. Both men and women tend to blame low desire on hormones or being too busy from work or tired from taking care of the kids to want sex.

While this may be the answer for a small number of women and men, the truth is that so many people are having sex that doesn't even begin to touch on their Core Desires. The question they are asking shouldn't be "Why am I losing my desire for sex?" the questions should be, "Why would anybody want to have sex that doesn't actually turn them on?"

When Jessica and Sanjay came to us, Jessica was not interested in sex at all. She didn't understand what the big deal was or why Sanjay was always grabbing at her. Growing up, she never masturbated and she felt that sex was something that other people did. Throughout her life there had been a few times she was aroused, once when she was reading the book Lolita for a college class and she masturbated all the time, the second time was when her friends all decided to read 50 Shades of Grey. She said the book was terrible, but she wanted to have sex with Sanjay all the time while she was reading it. Once she was done with the books, she lost her interest again.

Sanjay was a gentle and loving man and was very happy to give her her space to explore. He loved the feeling of mutuality. He wanted to take turns giving and receiving pleasure and feel that he and his partner both deeply desired sex. He loved the idea of pleasing his partner when it was his turn to give. He was very polite and often asked her what she wanted or whether she liked what he was doing. While Jessica really loved Sanjay, she didn't understand why she wasn't interested in having sex with him. After all, he was a very kind and patient lover and gave her orgasms whenever they ended up having sex.

When we started to bring up the idea of what she wanted to feel during sex, she said that she didn't have any fantasies. However, she was able to point to the movies and the literature that aroused her. As we delved deeply into what excited her about books like 50 Shades of Gray and Lolita, she said that she felt like sex or sexual tension just happened to the main characters. She said she didn't really like to think about sex or talk about it too much because, as she put it, "I don't want it to be my fault."

As a young child, she felt like she could do no right with her parents and she was always getting in trouble. Her punishments were relatively severe and included physical punishments such as spanking and doing extra chores as well as losses of many privileges. Additionally, her family was very shaming around sex and she knew she would get in particular trouble if she were to do anything sexual. At first, we thought Jessica wanted to be dominated into sex, but as she tried different experiences, what she actually found was that she wanted to feel *innocent*. In their earlier sex together, when Sanjay asked her what she would like during sex, she immediately felt like she had been caught having sex and her body shut down fearing punishment.

As Sanjay learned how to take Jessica without asking, reading her body cues to make sure she was having pleasure and whispering the right things in her ear, their sex life became way more exciting. Jessica's favorite phrases were anything in the vein of "There's nothing you can do about it and it's not your fault, I'm going to have sex with you now." She said, blushing, that her pussy would get immediately very wet. After this kind of seduction, her arousal took over and she was excited enough to both give and receive, so Sanjay was able to get his desire for mutuality met as well.

Porn Dependence

Many men worry that they are becoming dependent on porn. Their female partners may also see their porn-watching as a problem. We have a unique way to look at porn use in general. What we've seen is that porn can help both men and women really dial down on what turns them on. If you watch porn, you probably understand. Just think about what search terms you type in or what kinds of interactions really get you going, this is a great hint about your Core Desires.

If the sex that you are having doesn't really align with any of your search terms, at least the porn you are watching does. If you put the shaming and the challenges around porn aside for a second, and bring curiosity to why a person in (or out) of a relationship may become dependent on porn as their main sexual outlet, one common reason is that their sex life lacks any ignition of their Core Desires.

As we said earlier, porn is the heroin of sex, so you can get a very strong dose of the feeling you want to have without having to ask, or teach, or negotiate for it at all. You also never have to risk shame or judgment from a partner, unless they happen to stumble on some porn you've been watching. Additionally, even if you do ask your partner for what you want and teach them, you still might not get the level of arousal you do from porn.

While porn can be a wonderful addition to your individual and couples sex life, there can be some negative ramifications of porn-watching. Firstly, if you are single, the widespread availability of porn may make you less motivated to go out and find a partner, even if you feel like you want to. If you are in a relationship, the intense arousal that comes from porn may make it more difficult for you to get aroused or erect during partnered sex.

At some point, you may have tried to quit porn in order to minimize any negative impact of porn on your dating or partnered sex life. While we've seen many men try to quit porn, we haven't seen many succeed. Even when you feel very strongly that having or keeping your relationship is more important than porn and promise yourself over and over again that you will quit watching, you may not be able to.

If you try and do not succeed, you might end up in a shame spiral. A shame spiral is when you go through a loop around trying to change a habit you feel is shameful such as porn watching. You try to quit, but then end up watching another video. Then you feel like you've screwed everything up so what's the point and you watch some more. Then, you beat yourself up about it and try again to quit. People can repeat this negative cycle many times, their self-esteem often spiraling down in the process.

Garrett and Whitney came to see us after Garrett accidentally left incest porn up on his computer screen. In their first session together, Whitney began listing all of the things that upset her about finding this video. Tears were streaming down her face when she shared, "First of all, we hardly ever have sex and, when we do, I don't feel like Garrett is really that into it. The porn was about brothers and sisters having sex with each other and now I'm afraid he's actually attracted to his sister. And, the sex was so upsetting. The sister was trying to make her brother stop, but the brother just kept pushing her and pushing her until eventually she gave in and enjoyed it."

Garrett was hanging his head in shame as we interrupted Whitney's litany. Over the course of the next few sessions, we did some individual work with Whitney to help her offload all of her fears so that she could stop shaming Garrett. In couples sessions, we helped them understand how Core Desires and Hottest Sexual Movies are formed.

Finally, Garrett had a safe enough space, and he began to share about his family dynamic. Until age 5, his father had been a workaholic. He spent almost no time with his son, coming home most nights after Garrett was asleep. When he was five, his little sister was born and, when she was two, Garrett's father was laid off from his job. Instead of going right back to work, he spent much more time with his family. Garrett was already in school and his father stayed home all day playing with his little sister.

Garrett felt jealous and neglected as he saw his sister get tons of love and attention from this man who he'd barely even gotten to know. Many years later, when he stumbled on incest porn, he was shocked at how strong of an arousal response he got. In a later session, he admitted to Whitney that he had started with father-daughter porn. He felt that watching it somehow made him feel *included*. Later, he realized that brother-sister porn also did the trick. He was not attracted to his actual sister, but brother-sister porn made him feel like he got to connect with the prized person in his family - his sister.

He realized that the particular porn he liked - where the sister resisted at first, but then succumbed to the brother's seduction - gave him the feeling that he would have been *included* if only anyone had actually seen how much fun he could be. The fact that the sister resists at first, but then gives in to the seduction and actually enjoys herself with her brother feels like proof of this.

Since Whitney's Hottest Sexual Movie was a very mainstream fantasy of being taken out on the town and wined and dined, which made her feel *wanted* and *cherished*, she was quite shocked and overwhelmed by her partner's desires at first. Eventually, as she started to understand how fantasies develop, and to realize that Garrett didn't really want sex with his sister, she was able to open up to the idea of him occasionally watching porn. When she was feeling particularly turned on by getting her own movie, she would even whisper in Garrett's ear, "Just imagine I'm your sister right now, I didn't want to have sex with you at first, but I didn't realize how good you were..." and other sentences that touched on Garrett's Core Desires.

Even if your sex life is full of what turns you on, you still may want to watch a bit of porn here and there. You may also try adding non-porn masturbation to your weekly routine. Masturbating to your own fantasies or seeing if you can get aroused just by stimulating your body can keep you more sensitized and ready for partner sex. You might also try masturbating without ejaculation, and see if that helps keep you motivated for dating and partnered sex.

Sexless Marriage or Low-Sex Marriage (Including Marriages That Have 'Lost the Spark')

The most common reason that couples and some married individuals come to see us is that they have a sexless relationship, have sex infrequently, or have sex that is boring and repetitive. They usually talk about being exhausted and prioritizing everything else over sex. When we dig a bit deeper, there is generally some kind of discrepancy in the kinds of sex they want to have. Since there are so many different ways people want to feel and different things people want to get out of sex, it is very likely that any two people who get together will have different Core Desires and Different Hottest Sexual Movies that they want to play out.

When there is a lack of understanding about the need to be more open and clear with their partners about what they want or if they believe that sex is just supposed to happen then it is likely they will end up playing out the Hottest

Sexual Movie of whoever prioritizes sex more in the relationship. In this case, the person who has a lower interest in sex in the first place will end up having sex that they don't like very much and therefore wanting sex even less, sometimes getting to a place of full avoidance or having duty sex. Usually, this leads to neither partner getting their needs met as both of them start to feel unloved and uncared for even though this isn't what is really going on.

In working with couples, we help them get to the bottom of what they want to feel and what kinds of experiences they want to have to get there. After all, if the sex you are getting is not really the sex you want, why wouldn't you prioritize everything else over sex? On the other hand, if you can't stop thinking about how hot your last sexual experience was, you will be much more likely to jump at the chance of having it again. To create this, you will need to enhance your sexual compatibility.

Enhance Your Sexual Compatibility

Now that you have begun to really honestly share your Core Desires with one another and are trying to learn how to give each other your Hottest Sexual Movies, you have probably started to notice how much inherent sexual compatibility you have with your partner. No two people are 100% sexually compatible; however, you may have found a partner with sexual desires that are a good match for you.

If you already have a high level of sexual compatibility with your partner, consider yourself lucky. This is much more rare than people think. If you happen to be lucky in this way, sharing more specifically about your Core Desires and Hottest Sexual Movies will help you make sex even more delicious than it already was.

One example of high sexual compatibility would be a couple where one of them wants to feel *competent* or that *they are an amazing lover* and the other wants to feel *taken*. The one who wants to feel like a great lover will probably have all sorts of creative ways to seduce their partner and give them pleasure, while the one who wants to be taken can lay back and enjoy the ride.

Another example of highly compatible Core Desires is someone who wants to *dominate* getting together with someone who wants to feel *pleasing* or *punished*. Some dominants get off on the idea that their sub is there to follow their every whim, and a person who wants to feel like they are pleasing will want to do it right for their dom. Other dominants like the idea of taking their submissive to task and some subs want to feel like they are naughty and in need of punishment, thus making them highly compatible.

However, sometimes a dominant and submissive will get together but have less compatible Hottest Sexual Movies. For example, some submissives want to be *unruly* and *fight back* against what their dominant wants. If a dominant wants a very subservient, agreeable submissive, this is much less compatible. A couple might be even more incompatible if they come to find that they are both dominant or both submissive and neither wants to switch.

Other incompatibilities can be a person who wants to feel really *safe* during sex and a person who wants to have *wild, risky* sex. Or, if one person is into quickies and the other person would rather have sex that lasts for hours. Another one we've seen in our offices are couples where one wants more than anything to be their partner's *one and only* and their partner is most interested in multi-partner sex like threesomes or orgies.

If you realize that you are a couple who has felt less compatible so far, all is not lost! It is still possible to have an extremely hot sex life by increasing your sexual compatibility. There are two ways you can do this. The first is called "bridging." In bridging, you get creative with your Hottest Sexual Movies and try to find ways to play sexually together that get to both of your Core Desires at the same time. In other words, there may be ways that you can have sex that you haven't even tried, which will give each of you the feelings you really want to have during a single sexual experience.

Once you try bridging, if you find that there is no way to have sex that hits both of your Core Desires at the same time, another option is turn-taking. Turn-taking can happen during the same sexual interaction or on different days. In turn-taking, you first focus on playing out one partner's Hottest Sexual Movie and then you go to the other person's Hottest Sexual Movie. While you may have a strong desire to bridge your movies, it can sometimes be much more fulfilling to take turns, because then each person gets the full experience of what they want and never have to feel like it is being watered down. The best solution may be to sometimes bridge and sometimes take turns.

Sexual Compatibility Through Bridging

Bridging means finding a shared Hottest Sexual Movie that meets both of your Core Desires. In order to find this shared Hottest Sexual Movie, you need to see if you can engage in an experience that offers each of you what you want to feel.

Here's one example of how we helped a couple to bridge their different Hottest Sexual Movies:

Jordan and Tammy's Bridging Journey

We had a beautiful couple - Jordan and Tammy - come to our office in a huge amount of distress. When they came in, Jordan felt very rejected and unloved and Tammy felt shut down and uncared for. They had a young child and Tammy was still on maternity leave. They were in couples' therapy for a while before coming to see us and had learned communication skills. They were happy that they were fighting less, but the sex still hadn't gotten any better because they'd never talked about their actual turn-ons.

As we started to delve into the feelings they wanted to have and dove into the Hottest Sexual Movie conversations and practice sessions, we found that very passionate sex made Jordan feel *wanted*. It meant a lot to him that Tammy showed her desire for him by accepting his passionate advances. He dreamed of Tammy touching him frequently throughout the day and wished she'd reciprocate wholeheartedly when he grabbed her and pulled her in for a kiss.

Tammy was interested in Jordan and loved him deeply, but what she wanted was to feel *cared for*. When Jordan approached her trying to sweep her off her feet with passion, she always felt attacked and not ready. When he approached her forcefully, she felt bypassed and accused Jordan of not taking her needs into account. Of course, there was nothing that Jordan wanted more than to help Tammy see that he truly wanted to take her needs into account, but he had no idea how to do it.

It was essential to help both of them see that this was not about a lack of love or desire between them, in fact, it was not personal at all. We pointed out that it was simply that they had different Hottest Sexual Movies and that so many couples suffer because of these same kinds of misunderstandings. It took a while, but when they finally accepted their pursuit of their Core Desires was about self-expression as opposed to rejecting their partner, it was hugely relieving. They began to see how much they loved and needed each other, but that their movies had a different pace and flavor.

We helped them move beyond any shame for their desires, emphasizing that their Core Desires developed in each of them a long time ago. And, importantly, that the differences were not anyone's' fault, nor did it mean that they weren't meant for each other. This helped them relax, connect, and stay present and excited in the hunt for a Hottest Sexual Movie that would work for both of them. They were also lucky in that neither of their Hottest Sexual Movies was very complex, or something that they didn't want to give each other. We helped them translate each other's hints and cues so that they could both get their Hottest Sexual Movies met at the same time.

Tammy's Hottest Sexual Movie started even before they were in the bedroom. It meant a lot to her when Jordan would come home, take the baby for a little while, and do some chores around the house. This gave Tammy time to relax and get back into her own body after spending all day with their baby. It also made Tammy feel that Jordan really cared about her, which was the best foreplay as far as she was concerned.

Then, when they got some time for themselves, it turned her on and relaxed her when Jordan was willing to slow down his pace, look in her eyes and tell her how much she meant to him, and how much he wanted to make sure that she was having a good time. Slowing down and checking in with her about her enjoyment meant a lot to Tammy.

When they started at this slower pace, Tammy felt much more turned on and connected, causing the pace of her arousal to increase, which met Jordan's need for immediacy and intense desire. She was able to go after Jordan and meet his desire for more physicality and intensity. It was important to Tammy that, even during this more intense phase, Jordan would check in with her once in a while on how she was doing so that she didn't feel bypassed. When he did that, Tammy would feel Jordan's strong investment in making sure she got her Hottest Sexual Movie and she became even more turned on and animalistic, further stoking Jordan's fire!

Pathways to Bridging

If you want to explore the possibility of bridging your desires, there are a few ways to go about this. Once you have shared your Core Desires and Hottest Sexual Movies and you have seen that there are differences, you need to see if there are parts of each of your movies that you both enjoy. This may mean you need to let go of the idea that sex has to go a specific way or have all of the elements you want to have in it.

When trying to bridge, it is important to start by focusing on the feelings that you each want to have (Core Desires) and not on the Hottest Sexual Movie. You will need to get creative and be willing to see if it is possible to meet the feeling without all of the actions that you thought needed to be met.

Getting Enough (But Not All) of Your Hottest Sexual Movie

One way to bridge is to let yourself start with the smallest act that gives you the feeling you want to have, while still making sure that there is enough of the feeling that you need in the mix.

Simon and Florette came to us a few months before they were about to get married. They were young and in love, but Simon was worried that he wouldn't be able to get his sexual needs satisfied in the relationship. He wanted to feel *powerful* and his fantasies of feeling powerful had always been about bondage. He had also been watching bondage porn since he was a teenager. He was fascinated by bondage and wanted to do it properly, the way he saw in porn.

When we ventured deeper into his Core Desires, Simon shared that what made him feel *most powerful* was when Florette was *helpless*. Florette didn't mind feeling helpless, but the bondage process felt painful and she really didn't like how long it took. Even with these drawbacks, Florette said she loved Simon and had been willing to participate in bondage once in a while.

Florette shared vulnerably about wanting to feel *precious and special* - she wanted Simon to treat her with *tenderness*. In her Hottest Sexual Movie, she imagined Simon telling her how beautiful she was and how his love for her was eternal. When she felt like Simon's focus was on the ropes he was tying instead of on her, she started to feel that he didn't love her; his love was his bondage routine. Over time she started to recoil from Simon's touch in general and she lost interest in sex. She felt far from *special, seen,* or *important,* let alone *precious* and there was no *tenderness* in his approach.

As we started to dig in and see what was essential to Simon, Florette felt relieved to find that Simon could let go of needing to be so methodical every time he tied her up.

Simon was also extremely relieved to hear that Florette wasn't against bondage itself, just the placement of attention on the ropes as opposed to her. Once we established what both of them needed and relieved their fears of sex having to be a particular way every time, we were able to find lots of ways to bridge.

Florette asked Simon to find smooth, soft, velvety ties, which felt much more *tender* to her and it made her feel *special* that Simon was willing to search for just the right ties for her. She also asked him to untie her while they were having intercourse, so she would be comfortable. Simon found that he enjoyed telling Florette how special and beautiful she was while he tied her up and that it somehow enhanced his fantasy about her being helpless. He liked that she needed his words to make her feel *precious* and *loved*.

He also expressed his disappointment that Florette didn't want to participate in the longer, more methodical tying process. He said he didn't need it all the time, but would feel a pretty significant loss if he never got to do it again. We talked about them taking time to apply the new bridging approach and practice it for a while so that Florette could have some time getting her Hottest Sexual Movie and let go of her resentment about having felt unimportant.

Over time, Florette began to feel more connected to Simon and they were able to sometimes bridge and sometimes do turn-taking (which we will talk about soon). When it was time to do turn-taking, Florette was open to the longer tying process when it was Simon's turn as long as she knew she was going to get his full adoration and care on her nights.

Bridging by Trying a Whole Different Movie

Another option for bridging is to find a completely different Hottest Sexual Movie that you've never tried before that meets each of your Core Desires. Oftentimes, people don't have any idea of what's on the menu for them sexually so they get stuck trying to do something their partner doesn't want without realizing that there may be other ways to get the feeling you want to have - ways that you haven't even considered yet.

Angelina and Dana came to us after having been together for 19 years. Throughout most of their relationship, they'd had sex about once a week and both of them felt happy about it. Recently, however, Angelina had attended a weekend workshop on women's orgasms where she'd learned about the many pathways to having multiple orgasms. She learned that she could be much more sexually responsive than she ever thought. She wanted to teach Dana and wanted them to have more sex.

Dana, on the other hand, wasn't feeling very interested in sex at all. She admitted that she was having it mostly for Angelina and had been for quite some time. Like many women, she chalked her low desire up to menopause and had been promising Angelina for months that she would get her hormones checked. Finally, Angelina insisted that they come in and talk to us and she asked that they each have a few sessions separately. We sometimes start separately when talking with couples, especially if it seems like one or both of them will not be forthcoming in front of the other.

Angelina came in first, gushing about her new discoveries. She said she had always felt that there was so much more to sex but had not had a lot of experience before Dana. She also said that she always felt like she was more turned on and attracted to Dana than she felt like Dana was to her. She said every once in a while Dana would come out of her shell and they'd have a wild night - usually when they were out of town and a lot of alcohol was involved, but that she really didn't know what Dana wanted.

When Dana first came in, she seemed embarrassed to be talking about sex at all, and kept saying the same thing over and over, "Sex is just different for me, I never really needed it that much and now my body seems to be done, too." When we started to talk with her about the concept of Core Desires, she said she preferred to just focus on sensations and not think about anything. That's when Celeste decided to share her fantasies about non-consent and the different kinds of sexual experiences around dominance and submission that had been arousing.

Dana seemed uncomfortable at first saying that she wanted sex to be consensual and that she also didn't think what she wanted would be something anyone would want to do. Slowly, but surely, she started to open up about the fact that she got most turned on when she thought about scenes of *degradation*. She said that in the lesbian community, she was surrounded by feminists and that she believed in equality, but that the things that turned her on most were *degrading* scenes in movies. She'd seen one movie as a teenager where a woman had cow dung thrown at her. Dana went home and masturbated and then spent the rest of the day crying, feeling like there was something terribly wrong with her.

We were grateful to have a few individual sessions with her before presenting her fantasies to Angelina. We wanted to make sure that she could let go of the shame about her Core Desires and get a really good idea of what might turn her on the most - whether or not Angelina was game. After trying a few different kinds of approaches, Dana found that she was most turned on by verbal degradation. She wanted to hear that *she was nothing*, that she *deserved to be used*, and that she was *going to get what was coming to her*. In the third session, when we experimented with offering her some of this language, she said that it was the most turned on she had ever been in a sexual experience with another person.

When Dana and Angelina were ready, we set up the ground rules for them to have a conversation about their Core Desires and Hottest Sexual Movies. It turned out that Angelina wanted to feel *important*, and particularly that *her needs were important*. When Dana said that she wanted to be *degraded*, Angelina flinched a little but stuck with it. We had prepared her for the idea that Dana might be scared to tell her and ashamed, and Angelina did the best she could to fully listen to and accept how Dana wanted to feel and the words that she wanted to hear.

While Angelina got to a place where she felt she could really understand and support Dana in her Core Desires, she felt completely hopeless when it came to giving her her Hottest Sexual Movie. Angelina was very invested in being authentic and just couldn't get the words out of her mouth that Dana wanted to hear. Dana definitely felt Angelina's needs were important, and wanted to learn all about her new orgasms, as long as she could also feel turned on in this new way that she had just discovered.

We tried a few different ideas, offering that Angelina could role-play a different person to degrade Dana, but she couldn't take other roles seriously. We tried playing with pain play to see if that felt degrading to Dana, but it didn't touch her Core Desires. It wasn't until we came up with a little bit of a game that we found a bridge that would work for both of them.

It started with Angelina trying to teach Dana something new that she wanted Dana to do to her. Dana would then try but purposefully get it wrong. This experience created enough of a sense of frustrated desire in Angelina that she could give Dana some degrading punishments. She would send Dana to the edge of the closet or the floor at the foot of the bed and tell her to stay there until she could do something right. While these weren't at all the words that Dana had come up with, she found the punishments and the firmness in Angelina's voice to be enough to touch her hot buttons.

Standing in the closet or lying at the foot of the bed would turn Dana on so much that when she was released from her punishment, she would spend hours learning and perfecting each new need Angelina shared.

Bridging Through Solo or Shared Fantasies

One way that people are unconsciously bridging all the time is by fantasizing about something that hits their Core Desires while they are having sex with a partner. This is something that you can do on your own without sharing it with your partner by just running the fantasy inside of your head. It is also something that you can do overtly by telling your partner the fantasy or having them tell it to you.

Sudeet had always had the fantasy of group sex. In his fantasies, he imagined piles of writhing, naked bodies and he was in the middle of it all. Everywhere he turned in his fantasies there were legs, breasts, and pussies and his fingers and tongue and penis and even his toes would be caressing and penetrating and feeling all of the flesh and sexual energy around him. His Core Desires were to feel *surrounded, dissolved, and received*. He had never shared these fantasies with his wife but had made jokes about group sex and sex parties.

His wife, Arthi, felt very disconnected like he was somewhere else during sex. She felt like he was touching her body, but he did so with his eyes squeezed shut and she never had a sense that he was with her. When she finally heard about his fantasies, she said she could relate to the feelings he wanted to have. It turned out that, at the feeling level, she also very much liked the idea of being *dissolved* and *surrounded* - though she felt much more comfortable with a more spiritual pathway, like being surrounded by energy or gods. She also wanted to *deeply receive* Sudeet. Group sex, however, was a dealbreaker. She did not want to have sex with other people and she didn't want Sudeet to either.

When we offered up the idea of them talking about the fantasies together during sex, Arthi got very shy. "I don't think I'm going to be talking during sex," she said, "but I'm fine if Sudeet does." Sudeet was fine with the role of storyteller and was very excited at the thought that his stories might turn both of them on. He began coming up with more and more creative and adventurous stories for Arthi - stories full of naked gods and humans surrounding them and engaging with them all sorts of sexual experiences. It turned out that Arthi was way beyond feeling fine - she loved Sudeet's stories and was extremely turned on by her husband's deep, rich voice and the fact that his attention was fully focused on her and on making the stories as sexy and fun for her as he could.

 ## Exercise:
Try to Make a Bridge

Creating a bridge between two different Hottest Sexual Movies is a trial and error process and it takes time and patience to get a truly fulfilling bridge. Prepare for it not to be perfect and stay open and curious. Schedule a night where you take the time to share your Core Desires with each other and your Hottest Sexual Movies. It might take a few dates just for this process.

When you share your Hottest Sexual Movies, do it with as much detail as possible. Talk about and demonstrate the attitude, the acts, and the words, the setting, and clothing that will make it most hot for you. Include everything, even if it is not essential, but simply nice to have.

Explore and play with the possibilities of trying each of the following bridging options and see which one works best for you:

1. Getting enough of your Hottest Sexual Movie

2. Trying a whole different movie

3. Shared fantasies

4. Solo fantasies

See what was enough for each of you and what worked. Make course corrections until you find ways that you can both be satisfied and have as much of your Hottest Sexual Movies as possible in the mix.

Sexual Compatibility Through Turn-Taking

While some couples have movies that are similar enough that it is possible to bridge the two movies into one sexual experience, other people have such different movies that they are not bridgeable. The difference may be in the mood, setting, clothes, attitude, experience, etc., but, regardless, they are just not able to find a sexual experience that hits both of their Core Desires at the same time. In this situation, a couple may end up with much more fulfillment by practicing turn-taking instead of bridging.

Turn-taking is essential when the two people in a couple have such vastly different movies that there is no way to bridge the two, but can also be a great option if each person wants to get their full movie without any distractions or tweaks. In other words, bridging is not better than turn-taking. Even if your movies are similar enough to bridge, you still might want to do some turn-taking so that each person can get exactly what they want. Knowing it is your night can give you a lot of permission to make it just right, and ask for what you want throughout the whole experience.

One Couple's Turn-Taking Journey

Anders and Brenda were a couple who were in a lot of distress about their sex lives. They were still having occasional sex, but neither one of them was very happy with the quality or quantity. Prior to coming to see us, they had arrived at a standstill around their sex life.

Anders and Brenda came to us after having read *Making Love Real* and having some inkling that they might have different Hottest Sexual Movies. They did not have any idea what to do about it and there had been a lot of misunderstanding, judgment, and resentment built up that needed to be sorted through before any sexiness was possible.

After much sorting and airing of frustration, rejection, and pain, the story unfolded. It turned out that Brenda was very interested in *novelty*, and liked to switch back and forth between being the more submissive and more dominant partner. Anders' Hottest Sexual Movie was quite regimented and he never wanted to be dominated, only to dominate.

At first this was fine, because his movie was novel for her - Brenda had never been tied up or spanked and dressing up in sexy clothes was also an exciting new adventure. She did like to be dominated as long as she felt his leadership was backed by kindness and a desire to include and respect her.

As they moved into a long-term relationship, and they started to have occasional conflicts as every couple does, Brenda became wary and suspicious whenever she felt Anders might be taking any actual anger out on her when he dominated her in bed. Additionally, she realized that he was not interested in getting creative with his movie. What really turned him on about it was going through each of the three phases of the movie and being able to fully get into the rhythm of the experience. Because it was a formula, he could move through it without having to think too much. He said it was "like playing a perfect Bach concerto from start to finish."

Because Brenda's Hottest Sexual Movie was about novelty, and her lovers before her husband had been flexible in their lovemaking style, she judged Anders as being immature. She hoped he would grow out of what she thought of as his rigidity. At the same time, she tried to meet bits and pieces of his movie during their other sexual experiences. Brenda's attempts to incorporate parts of Anders' movie only served to frustrate him because he felt like she was trying to wean him away from his desires. He started to worry that he would never get his full movie again.

Additionally, Brenda pointed out that the sex they had been having for years was what she called "regular" sex, and she was upset at the idea that Anders might think she was actually getting her Hottest Sexual Movie met. At the same time, Brenda felt it was very important that they have a sex life regardless of what kind of sex. She said sex was deeply important to her feeling of day-to-day bonding in the relationship.

As we talked through the way our Core Desires work and explained that they generally don't change, some of the judgment started to fall away. They started to see that they had very different, and in some ways, quite opposite movies. We suggested that it was going to be much better to approach their sex life with a turn-taking model as opposed to trying to bridge their two movies.

The goal was to create a sex life for the two of them where each of them could get their movie. Once we focused on turn-taking, we explored ways that Brenda would get to feel included and satisfied engaging in the full experience of Anders' movie. When it was her turn, Brenda wanted novelty, which for her meant nearly anything out of the ordinary. A surprise sexual rendezvous on the deck or a night out to a show followed by renting a hotel room gave her the rush of excitement she needed. She could escape the monotony and responsibility of the day-to-day obligations that came from having four kids and a gaggle of pets.

Eventually, Brenda and Anders needed to negotiate the specifics of their movie. In order to be willing to play Anders' movie, Brenda needed for him to have a dominant persona like George Clooney - witty, confident, and a bit playful, but not at all mean. She also wanted him to talk more because it helped her feel more connected. Unfortunately, Anders felt himself pulled out of the yumminess of his trance-like state when he spoke, so we looked for other ways for him to signal that he was there with her. They both liked a lot of eye contact and Brenda felt she would feel him there with her if he looked her in the eyes and also gave her a lot of firm, grabbing touch. He also agreed to talk sometimes.

We hope you can see from this negotiation that turn-taking doesn't mean you have to do exactly what your partner wants if it makes you uncomfortable. Instead, each person asked for what they wanted, talked about what would work for them and wouldn't, and then found ways to get as much of their movie met as possible. Neither Brenda nor Anders got exactly what they wanted in their sex life, but it was so much closer than they had been able to get to without this turn-taking model. They started having more sex and more physical affection, and hardly ever fought about their sex life.

 ## Exercise:
Have a Turn-Taking Week

Pick two date nights in a week and assign one to each of you. When it is your night to get your movie:

Share your Core Desires and your Hottest Sexual Movie with as much detail as possible. You may want to write it up for your partner and send it in advance via email so they start to get the picture. When you have your date night, talk and demonstrate the attitude, the acts, and the words, setting and clothing that will make it most hot for you. Include everything, even if it is not essential, but simply nice to have.

See what is interesting for the other person to do and what turns them on the most. See what they are willing and able to do. Experiment with teaching and learning by following the steps in How to Teach Your Partner Your Hottest Sexual Movie. Pay attention to what was enough for you and what worked. Make course corrections until you find ways that you can be satisfied and as much of your Hottest Sexual Movie as possible is in the mix.

Generosity can be a turn on. Throughout the process of playing out your partner's Hottest Sexual Movie, try to be fully engaged and enjoy yourself as much as possible. Think about how engaged you want them to be as they give you your movie. It is possible that you will find it challenging to get turned on when it is your movie because you might be worried that your partner isn't fully in it. Think about how amazing it is that each of you is willing to get out of your comfort zone, be generous, and give each other your movies. This may really help with your turn-on.

What If You Can't Attain Sexual Compatibility?

We hope that *Coming Together* has at least helped you to accept your partner for who they are and to stop blaming and shaming each other for something that you have no control over - your Core Desires. We also hope that understanding and sharing your desires with one another has deepened your connection and intimacy.

We believe that it is our job as sex and relationship coaches to support adults in seeing and accepting the reality that they are choosing, and choosing that reality consciously and without resentment. Thus, if both people in a couple share that they are choosing to stay in a sexually unfulfilling relationship, and that they are making this choice in the face of true soul-searching, we think that is wonderful. There are so many aspects to a relationship that might be important to people. These include love, emotional support, co-parenting, financial support, familial connection, and the many other gifts of long-term relationships.

At the same time, if one or both of you do feel sex is very important, we strongly suggest that you do not try to deny this need as it will continue to boil under the surface and cause many problems in your relationship. It is much better to be honest up front before this lack causes so much distance and resentment that you no longer feel connected to a person you love and care about.

In order to make these decisions, we suggest you start with processing disappointment.

Processing Disappointment to Find Acceptance

If you feel like you have tried everything you can to shift your sexual dynamic and you still don't feel sexually satisfied, the first thing you will need to do is to decide how much of a priority sex is for you. You do this by acknowledging and processing your disappointment.

It may be that having a fulfilling sex life is not your priority, at least for the time being, and that is fine. When people say that sex is not a priority, the thing we always want to check on is if one or both people in the relationship are de-emphasizing the importance of sex in their lives out of shame. Because our culture trivializes sex, people for whom sex is a high priority often feel embarrassed to assert how essential a sexual outlet is for them.

We think it is quite sad that people feel like they have to get everything that they need in one relationship and, if they don't, that the relationship is a failure. We believe many marriages and long-term relationships can continue to thrive if people let go of this idea and realize that they may or may not decide to get needs met elsewhere, but that it doesn't mean that they have failed if they cannot get all of their needs met from one person.

It may be that feeling fully accepted by your partner and being able to process through your disappointment about having an unsatisfying or nonexsistent sex life is enough. Through the process of understanding and accepting each other, you may feel more deeply seen and loved than you thought possible. You may decide that you want to stay in the relationship as it is, knowing that the disappointment could come up again and that you will need to face it if and when it arises.

While there are no statistics to tell you how much of your needs you can expect to have met in your relationship, we sometimes introduce the idea of the 70/30 rule. It is impossible to expect that anyone will be 100 percent of what we want all the time (no matter how many Hollywood movies try to tell us otherwise). It is possible that someone could be 70 percent of what you want. This leaves 30 percent disappointment and some of this 30 percent may come in the sexual realm. A relationship that tries to avoid all disappointment probably won't survive, as the couple's attempts to avoid disappointing each other will feed their resentment and drive them further and further apart. But love definitely can survive disappointment. It does so all the time.

If you are like most folks in relationships, you are constantly trying to avoid or manage your own or your partner's disappointment without ever directly acknowledging or sharing it. If you have come to the realization that your sex life is not going to be what you want it to be and one or both of you are disappointed, it can be very powerful to have a connected disappointment conversation.

We have found that allowing your partner to feel their disappointment while you stay and listen to them lovingly is the best way to stay connected through the inevitable challenges of long-term relationships, which include sexual challenges. Sharing and listening to disappointment without defending, apologizing, or trying to fix a problem that is not going to get fixed actually promotes trust, heals old wounds, deepens connection and intimacy, and fosters the resilience and longevity of the relationship.

To expand your skillset for listening and holding each other's disappointment, we recommend that you read our book for couples: *Making Love Real: The Intelligent Couples Guide to Lasting Intimacy and Passion*.

If you are able to process all of your disappointment, get out of resentment, and feel accepted by your partner, you will have a much better idea of whether or not sex is something you can live without. For some, it isn't always the sex that matters, and they might feel satisfied being a part of a sexual community. We worked with one couple, for example, where the man was willing to forgo his desire for kinky sex, as long as he was free to hang out with the kink community.

If you do feel very accepted by your partner, but still very much want to have a sex life, you can try the following:

Have "Warm Sex" Instead of Hot Sex

If you are in a relationship where you want to stay monogamous, Jack Morin offers up the idea of having "warm sex" instead of "hot sex". While that might not sound so great, it is also possible that you really want to stay in the relationship because there are very important needs it is meeting for you. You might feel that there are higher priorities for you than hot sex. Perhaps you have been able to find some ways that you can get each other off that don't touch your Core Desires, but that fulfill you enough to want to stay in the relationship.

Examples of warm sex might be giving each other an erotic massage. You can do this on a bed or buy a massage table. In this case, you will take turns focusing on how to give each other positive physical sensations and possibly orgasms as opposed to worrying about the psychological aspects of arousal. There are some excellent resources out there on how to give each other a great erotic massage, and you can focus on developing these skills.

Another option is side-by-side masturbation. By sharing a masturbation experience, you can still feel the nice after-effects of sexual arousal and release together and perhaps bring some touching or kissing into the mix as a warm-up and/or some cuddling afterward.

Have an Honest, Open Relationship

Some couples decide that, given all of the options, they prefer to have an honest, open relationship. There are many different reasons why people choose to have open relationships. Some people consider polyamory or nonmonogamy to be more of an orientation or identity, like being gay, lesbian, or bisexual. These folks may have multiple relationships regardless of any other factors. Other people choose to practice non-monogamy more situationally, perhaps because they have a partner who requests it, or because they want to meet some of the sexual or emotional needs that are missing from the relationship.

Also, some couples who have gone through the process of trying to create a satisfying sex life within their relationship and have not been able to do so, may decide to get some or all of their sexual needs met outside of the relationship. Some people do this by negotiating honest, open relationships or poly relationships, while others might choose to pursue their unmet sexual needs without sharing this information with their partner.

Like any significant relationship choice, including monogamy, getting some of your sexual needs met may make the relationship last longer or may precipitate a break-up. This is true whether you are outsourcing sexual needs honestly or dishonestly. Before we go any further, we want to point out that open relationships are often blamed for break-ups, however, when a monogamous relationship breaks up, we rarely hear anyone say, "Wow, that relationship really could have lasted if only they were not so stuck on the idea of monogamy."

Yet, monogamy could easily be a reason why a relationship between two people might not last. If a couple ends up in a sexless marriage with no option for getting their sexual needs met, they may indeed leave the relationship - a relationship that might have been preserved had they tried opening it up. We say this not because we are "pro-poly" or "pro-monogamy." We say it because there are a lot of cultural beliefs around what is the right or best way to have a relationship that people don't ever question. They simply follow the social norms, which may or may not fit well with their particular needs.

In our practice, we try to help people look at all of their options so that they can create the relationship structures that are right for them. We believe adults can handle having all of the possible alternatives on the table when making these choices. Instead of trying to force every person into the one box our culture offers - forever monogamy with one person - we help people explore which relationship structure might fit their specific emotional, familial, erotic, and identity needs. This includes supporting the option of choosing not to be in a relationship at all.

With all of that being said, there are reasons people choose to honestly negotiate an open relationship and reasons people choose to get their needs met without telling their partner. A person may choose the honest option because they feel it is safe to do so, because they are excited by the idea that they can explore together with their partner, or because they don't want to lie. A different person may choose to get their needs met without telling their partner because they are certain their partner will not accept them and they are not willing to risk losing their relationship or their children.

We suggest when you are talking through your choices, you at least have a conversation about the possibility of opening your relationship. See if you can make a safe space where both of you can express your feelings about this. Ultimately, you get to keep your boundaries and, if you do not want to open up, you don't have to. If you can talk through all of the options in a loving, connected way, it can be very clarifying. If you have no idea how to have this conversation, it may be good to get the help of a coach or therapist. If you do choose to work with a coach or therapist, make sure they are embracing and knowledgeable of all options.

Shift the Relationship

If, after trying everything within your boundaries - from learning each other to bridging, from processing disappointment to considering and possibly trying open relating - you still find that you are not getting your needs met and are not willing to live without a satisfying sex life, you may choose to shift the relationship.

One of the worst ramifications of our cultural belief that the only successful relationship is forever monogamy with one person is that amazing connections between people who love and care for each other, and who are each other's families, end up shattering in horrible ways instead of shifting. This paradigm leaves a wake of trauma for each of the people in the relationship, their children if they have any, and their friends and family members.

We truly believe that a successful relationship is one where people have stayed together in one relationship configuration for as long as it feels good and right for both of them, which may or may not be forever. Shifting into a different relationship configuration before it becomes horrible, and especially seeing if you can shift to a new relationship configuration lovingly with one another instead of having to demonize each other and "break" up, are signs of a successful relationship. In fact, approaching relationships this way feels like a much stronger commitment, because it means you are committed to staying connected and supporting one another in being true to yourselves throughout your lives.

The way that people feel about each other and what they need from each other always changes over time. If you do decide to shift into another relationship configuration as a result of these changes and to move into friendship, co-parenting, living together platonically, or something a bit more distant but still kind and connected, you may need some time apart to feel into what is the right relationship configuration for you after the shift. Finding the right configuration for you is an ongoing process where you allow for changes but stay in connection.

We Hope You Find the Right Choice for **You**!

In this section, we've talked about all of the different ways you can deal with differences in sexual compatibility from turn-taking to bridging and how to handle it if sexual compatibility is not in the cards for you. It is our ultimate hope that each person has as much love, affection, secure attachment, and sexual fulfillment as possible, with as little pain and trauma as possible. This is what we help individuals and couples work on every day in our offices. You are the expert on your own life and we hope this has helped you clarify what you want and how to best get it.

Follow Your Core Desires as a Way of Life

In *Coming Together* we have taken you on a journey to discover your Core Desires in the sexual realm. In essence, we are inviting you to move beyond the one-size-fits-all approach to sexual desire and embrace your beautifully unique desires as a guide to how you want to live as an erotic being in the world.

So, why stop with sex? If you take *Coming Together* as a guide for how to live your life in general, we hope you will see it points the way towards you discovering your true desires in every area of your life - family, work, education, community, etc. In our lives, we face judgments and expectations about who and how we are supposed to be from many different sources, including ourselves. What if, instead of listening to all of those judgments, you listened in closely to the voice of your desire?

Here's an example from our business. When we first developed our business, like good CEOs we made ourselves a business plan. We wrote our mission statement, our goals, our strengths and weaknesses, and we also wrote our core values. On top of our core values list was, "Makes me wet." We decided we didn't want to do anything in our business unless it truly excited us. We believe this has been the biggest key to our success.

When approaching decisions in your life, consider what path makes you feel most alive. Listen to exactly what makes you feel more connected to the people you love, what makes you feel most fully yourself, and what makes you want to jump out of bed in the morning, ready to dive into the beauty and the challenge that is your life. We hope you fully embrace every minute of it!

Made in the USA
Las Vegas, NV
29 March 2022

46510281R00105